THE NEW HUMAN REVOLUTION

VOLUME 20

THE NEW HUMAN REVOLUTION

VOLUME 20

DAISAKU IKEDA

ILLUSTRATIONS BY
KENICHIRO UCHIDA

World Tribune
—*Press*—

Published by World Tribune Press
606 Wilshire Boulevard
Santa Monica, California 90401

Complete Set ISBN: 978-0-915678-32-7
Volume 20 ISBN: 978-0-915678-52-5
Interior and cover designed by Gopa & Ted2, Inc.

10 9 8 7 6 5 4 3 2 1

Contents

Editor's Note

The citations most commonly used in this book have been abbreviated as follows:

◆ GZ, page number(s) refers to the *Gosho zenshu*, the Japanese-language compilation of letters, treatises, essays and oral teachings of Nichiren Daishonin.

◆ LSOC, page number(s) refers to *The Lotus Sutra and Its Opening and Closing Sutras*, translated by Burton Watson (Tokyo: Soka Gakkai, 2009).

◆ OTT, page number(s) refers to *The Record of the Orally Transmitted Teachings*, translated by Burton Watson (Tokyo: Soka Gakkai, 2004).

◆ WND, page number(s) refers to *The Writings of Nichiren Daishonin,* vol. 1 (WND-1) (Tokyo, Soka Gakkai, 1999) and vol. 2 (WND-2) (Tokyo: Soka Gakkai, 2006).

Path of Friendship

THE DOOR to a new age will not open as long as we wait for it to happen. We must open it ourselves, through our own dauntless and courageous actions. With this spirit, Shin'ichi Yamamoto set forth boldly.

At half past ten in the morning on May 30, 1974, the first Soka Gakkai delegation to China, led by Shin'ichi, boarded a train in Kowloon, Hong Kong—at that time a British territory—heading for the People's Republic of China.

In about an hour they arrived at Lo Wu, the last Hong Kong station, where they completed the necessary procedures for crossing the border. They walked about 330 feet from Lo Wu Station to Shenzhen Station on the other side. Japan–China relations had been normalized in 1972, but there was still no way to travel directly between the two countries. Even to travel to Beijing, the Chinese capital, one had to go by way of Hong Kong.

The delegation visiting China consisted of eleven members: delegation head Shin'ichi and his wife, Mineko; delegation vice head and Soka Gakkai vice president Hisaya Yamamichi; delegation secretary and Soka Gakkai student division leader Kaoru Tahara; Soka Gakkai young women's division leader Mikako Kitsukawa; an interpreter; a reporter and a photographer from the *Seikyo Shimbun*; and others. When the group arrived at Lo Wu, the rain that had followed them from Kowloon lifted, leaving a fine covering of cloud. Walking toward Shenzhen Station, Shin'ichi recalled his discussions with individuals who had devoted their lives to building bridges of friendship between Japan and China.

One such person was businessman and former Japanese Minister of International Trade and Industry Tatsunosuke Takasaki, who had been pivotal in establishing the L–T (Liao-Takasaki) Memorandum on Trade between the two countries in 1962. In September 1963, Mr. Takasaki told Shin'ichi: "I myself may not live to see Japan–China friendship happen. We need people with fresh energy and commitment in order to achieve it. I'm counting on you to contribute that energy to establishing amicable bilateral relations!" Mr. Takasaki was seventy-eight at the time. He died just five months later.

In March 1970, eighty-seven-year-old Kenzo Matsumura, a Japanese political leader earnestly devoted to improving relations between the two countries, urged Shin'ichi: "You should go to China. Yes, I'd like someone like you to go." Shin'ichi took the words of these two men as a legacy he would strive to fulfill, and he made it his personal mission to build a golden bridge of Japan–China friendship. Each step he took toward Shenzhen Station was filled with grave resolve.

AT THE BEGINNING of 1956, Shin'ichi's mentor, second Soka Gakkai president Josei Toda, had composed a poem that now reverberated in Shin'ichi's heart:

> *To the people of Asia*
> *who pray for a glimpse of the moon*
> *through the parting clouds,*
> *let us send, instead,*
> *the light of the sun.*

When Shin'ichi read that poem for the first time, he keenly sensed his mentor's passionate commitment to the peace and happiness of the people of Asia. That was also the sentiment that Mr. Toda often shared with him during their tutoring sessions, which Shin'ichi called "Toda University." Since then, Shin'ichi had been thinking seriously about what practical steps he could take as Mr. Toda's disciple to ensure the happiness of the people of China, Asia's largest nation. After much careful consideration, he concluded that one essential step was to establish friendly relations between Japan and China and open the way for bilateral exchange and positive interaction.

The great wish of the mentor could not be realized in a

single lifetime. It required that his disciples stand up with the same commitment and carry the effort on toward its completion. That is the mission of disciples, and the way the shared wish of mentor and disciple is achieved.

Shin'ichi had been waiting for the ideal moment to take action. Then, when the Clean Government Party was officially established in November 1964, he remarked: "I hope the Clean Government Party will adopt as part of its foreign policy platform the formal recognition of the People's Republic of China and the reestablishment of diplomatic relations with that country. That is my only request as the party's founder." In addition, at the 11th Student Division General Meeting held four years later, in September 1968, Shin'ichi offered his historic and momentous proposal publicly calling for the normalization of Japan–China diplomatic relations.

The proposal consisted of three main elements: (1) Japan's recognition of the People's Republic of China and the normalization of diplomatic relations with that country, (2) the restoration of China's status in the United Nations and (3) the promotion of bilateral economic and cultural exchange.

At that time, China was in the midst of the Cultural Revolution (1966–76), and world opinion was very critical of the country. Shin'ichi was well aware that calling for the reestablishment of bilateral relations as well as China's reentry into the United Nations at such a time would expose him to a concentrated volley of harsh attacks and criticism. But as the Chinese writer Lu Xun (1881–1936) once said, "Those who are ahead of their times are never accepted in their native land and indeed are persecuted by their contemporaries."[1]

SHIN'ICHI BELIEVED that world peace would hinge on the direction China took. This is because one of the major destabilizing factors threatening global peace at the time was the tumultuous situation in Asia, caused by poverty as well as the schism, mistrust and tension between the communist and capitalist blocs. Japan's initiative in building friendship with China was certain to relax East-West tensions as they were being played out in Asia. Convinced that this would eventually lead to the resolution of this standoff on a global scale, Shin'ichi made his proposal for the normalization of Japan–China relations.

Shin'ichi's proposal was reported in such major Japanese newspapers as the *Asahi Shimbun*, the *Yomiuri Shimbun* and the *Mainichi Shimbun*, and was wired to China as well. It aroused a tremendous response.

Yoshimi Takeuchi, a Japanese scholar of Chinese literature, lauded it as "a ray of light" in the movement to restore diplomatic relations. And when Kenzo Matsumura, a Japanese politician and longtime advocate of bilateral friendship, learned of the proposal, he remarked, "We have gained a multitude of allies.""

However, Shin'ichi's proposal also drew a storm of harsh criticism. People made threatening phone calls and sent angry letters, and some groups even put sound trucks on the streets to denounce the proposal over their loudspeakers. Others questioned why a religious leader should "don a red necktie"—in other words, show sympathy for a communist nation. Top officials in Japan's foreign ministry also expressed their strong disapproval.

But Shin'ichi was not afraid. One cannot truly fight for peace unless prepared to risk one's life. Far from being intimidated, Shin'ichi continued to speak out for improving relations between Japan and China. Having been trained by Mr. Toda, he had the spirit of a courageous lion.

In the December 1968 issue of the monthly academic journal *Asia,* Shin'ichi published an article titled "A Proposal for the Normalization of Japan–China Relations," in which he discussed his proposal in greater depth. And in June of the following year, he asserted in his novel *The Human Revolution* being serialized in the *Seikyo Shimbun* that not only should relations between the two countries be normalized, but every effort should be made to see that a friendship treaty was signed.

Just as the consistent pounding of waves erodes massive rocks, ceaseless efforts can surmount any barrier and achieve the impossible.

CHINESE PREMIER Zhou Enlai was closely observing Shin'ichi's advocacy of better Japan–China relations, keeping abreast of Shin'ichi's efforts in that sphere as well as the activities of the Soka Gakkai as a whole.

The Soka Gakkai had brought together and organized ordinary people, giving hope and a new lease on life to those lost in the depths of apathy and despair. It taught them a philosophy of life and about living with a sense of mission, fostering them into protagonists for positive social change. The flowers of peace and prosperity cannot bloom unless the earth of the people is well cultivated. The Soka Gakkai's strength came from being deeply rooted in the people, and the power of the people was becoming a new force in Japan. Perhaps it was inevitable that Premier Zhou should take note of the Soka Gakkai, which was in the forefront of this people's movement, and its youthful leader Shin'ichi.

For some time, Premier Zhou had demonstrated an active interest in Shin'ichi and the Soka Gakkai, encouraging those around him not only to learn more about the organization but also instructing them to work on opening a channel of communication with it. When the Japanese novelist Sawako Ariyoshi visited China, Premier Zhou told her that he hoped President Yamamoto would make a trip to the country in the future. He even entrusted her with a verbal invitation, which she conveyed on a visit to the Soka Gakkai Headquarters in Tokyo in May 1966.

In March 1970, Shin'ichi met with Kenzo Matsumura, who had long served as a pipeline between Japan and China. The latter enthusiastically encouraged Shin'ichi to go to China and said he would arrange a meeting between Shin'ichi and Premier Zhou. Shin'ichi understood Mr. Matsumura's position and deeply appreciated his offer, but he politely declined, feeling that the time was not yet ripe. China still in the turbulent throes of the Cultural Revolution, was strongly anti-religion. Shin'ichi thought that if he, a religious leader, were to visit China while this climate still prevailed, it would only cause problems for Mr. Matsumura as well as for his Chinese hosts.

In addition, he recognized that the normalization of diplomatic relations was fundamentally a political issue, and unless political leaders took the lead, it could not proceed smoothly. Shin'ichi explained all of this to Mr. Matsumura and suggested that Clean Government Party members visit China first.

AFTER HIS MEETING with Shin'ichi, Mr. Matsumura traveled to China and conveyed Shin'ichi's
thoughts in detail to Premier Zhou. The Chinese leader
entrusted Mr. Matsumura with the message that Shin'ichi
would be warmly welcomed whenever he decided to
visit China.

Clean Government Party representatives first went to
China the following year, in June 1971. At the outset of
their meeting with Premier Zhou, the latter kindly asked
them to give his personal regards to President Yamamoto.

During this visit, the Clean Government Party officials
issued a joint statement with members of the China–Japan
Friendship Association concerning the basic conditions
necessary for the restoration of diplomatic relations. There
were five main points, starting with the adoption of the

One-China policy, recognizing the People's Republic of China as the sole legal government of the whole of China. The joint statement was primarily based on the foreign policy of the Clean Government Party, which fully endorsed Shin'ichi's proposal for the normalization of bilateral relations. Shin'ichi also sensed Premier Zhou's sincere input in the statement.

Known as the "Five Principles for Restoring Relations," they became the guidelines for further intergovernmental negotiations. The wheels of the age were beginning to turn toward the realization of normalized Japan–China relations that Shin'ichi had earnestly been calling for.

Chinese revolutionary leader Sun Yat-sen said, "To accomplish a great enterprise, above all one must possess great will, great daring and great resolve."[2] Only by acting with courage and a lofty purpose can we achieve a momentous undertaking that will change the course of history.

Two weeks later, in mid-July, U.S. president Richard Nixon announced that he planned to visit China by the following May. This represented a significant change in U.S. policy in Asia, which had always viewed China as an adversary. And at the October 1971 session of the United Nations General Assembly, the People's Republic of China was recognized as China's sole legal government and invited to join the United Nations.

President Nixon visited China in February 1972, and the United States and China initiated steps toward restoring their diplomatic relations without consulting the Japanese government. Japan was in danger of being left behind in a major shift in world history. Thinking people came to recognize even more the importance of Shin'ichi's earlier groundbreaking steps.

IN JULY 1972, a new Japanese government was formed with Kakuei Tanaka as prime minister. The Clean Government Party sent delegations to China in May and July of that year. During the July visit, which took place immediately after the inauguration of the Tanaka administration, the Clean Government Party representatives acted as a pipeline for the Japanese government, carefully working with Premier Zhou over each of the concrete points for restoring bilateral relations.

The Japanese government's greatest concern regarding the normalization of relations was the issue of war reparations to China. In the eight years of hostilities in China starting in 1937, thirty-five million Chinese were killed or wounded, and China's direct and indirect economic losses were estimated at six hundred billion dollars.[3]

But in his talks with Clean Government Party representatives, Premier Zhou declared that China would not seek war reparations from Japan. He noted that when China was defeated by Japan in the first Sino-Japanese War (1894–95), it had to pay large reparations to Japan, and the heavy taxes forced upon the Chinese people to make that possible had been a punishing burden. The war, Premier Zhou said, was the responsibility of a handful of militarists, and the Japanese people were also their victims. He did not wish the Japanese people to suffer as the Chinese had in the past.

It is the way of the world that a nation seeks to retaliate when another nation inflicts harm on its people. But because of China's experience, Premier Zhou did not want to cause further suffering to the people of Japan. When Shin'ichi considered what a gift this was to the Japanese people, he felt profound gratitude toward the Chinese leader. *Japan must never forget this great act of generosity*, he thought.

Spanish author Miguel de Cervantes (1547–1616) wrote, "Ingratitude is the daughter of pride and one of the greatest sins known."[4]

Japan should also never forget that Japan–China friendship is founded on China's willingness to forgo war reparations based on the awareness that responsibility for the war rested with Japan's military leadership and that Japanese citizens were also victims.

At his final meeting with the Clean Government Party representatives in July 1972, Premier Zhou summed up what they had discussed thus far and read out the Chinese draft of a proposed joint China-Japan communiqué. The Clean Government Party officials took careful notes and after returning home conveyed them to Prime Minister Tanaka and Foreign Minister Masayoshi Ohira.

PREPARATIONS FOR the normalization of diplomatic relations between Japan and China had been completed. On September 25, 1972, a delegation of Japanese government officials led by Prime Minister Kakuei Tanaka visited China, and on the 29th, a joint declaration announcing the restoration of diplomatic relations was officially signed. At last, twenty-three years after the birth of the People's Republic of China, this long-awaited goal was realized.

Representatives of the China-Japan Friendship Association and the Xinhua News Agency clearly stated that

Shin'ichi's September 1968 proposal calling for the normalization of bilateral relations was the reason that the Clean Government Party was able to act as a go-between in this rapprochement. Chinese Premier Zhou Enlai, who held Shin'ichi's proposal in high regard, trusted the Clean Government Party because Shin'ichi had founded it.

Four years after Shin'ichi had made his proposal, the reestablishment of ties between Japan and China that he had eagerly anticipated was achieved. A bridge of friendship once again connected Japan and its close neighbor China, with which it had enjoyed a long history of exchange.

Courageous words can change the course of history. That is why it is crucial to speak out fearlessly for truth, justice and one's convictions.

Shin'ichi watched the television reports of this significant development with a profound inner resolve to forge this new connection with China into a broad and solid golden bridge linking the people of both nations.

After the restoration of Japan–China diplomatic relations, Shin'ichi received numerous requests to visit China. He, too, wanted to go there at the earliest opportunity. However, he was extremely busy with ceremonies commemorating the completion of the Sho-Hondo (Grand Main Temple) as well as preparing for his dialogue with British historian Arnold J. Toynbee and other matters, making it difficult to arrange a trip to China.

Toward the end of 1973, in response to a request by the China-Japan Friendship Association, Shin'ichi was finally able to agree to a visit. In March 1974, the Chinese Embassy in Tokyo officially conveyed China's invitation to Shin'ichi. From that time on, preparations for his trip to China began in earnest, but the exact schedule remained undecided.

On May 24, Shin'ichi received a telegram formally confirming the invitation from the China-Japan Friendship Association. It contained a detailed itinerary, with his departure date and schedule while in China.

ON THE MORNING of May 29, Shin'ichi and his party departed from Tokyo's Haneda International Airport. Shin'ichi expressed his appreciation to those who were on hand to see him off, including representatives from the Chinese Embassy in Tokyo, the Xinhua News Agency and the Japan-China Cultural Exchange Association.

He then remarked: "I will be visiting China at the invitation of the China-Japan Friendship Association for about two weeks. Political and economic exchanges sometimes result in discord because they are often motivated by power or self-interest. I am determined to make cultural exchange my top priority and to promote genuine friendship on the grassroots level in order to construct an everlasting and unshakable foundation for peace. In particular, recognizing that education is the wellspring of cultural growth and creativity, I hope to observe China's education system and engage in a frank exchange of opinions and ideas in this area.

"As most of the members of this delegation are youth, I hope to initiate exchange between them and the young people and students of China who will shoulder the future. I believe that this will in turn encourage mutual understanding as well as strengthen ties of trust and friendship among the youth of both nations."

Shin'ichi felt that the aim of diplomatic relations was not merely the exchange of goods but exchange between people. He was also certain that exchange between young people would open a path of friendship that would endure for centuries to come. He was deeply resolved to blaze a path for youth, a path leading to the far distant future.

Shin'ichi and his party arrived in Hong Kong shortly after two in the afternoon on May 29. They spent one night in Hong Kong, and the following morning departed from rainy Kowloon on the Kowloon–Canton Railway. Representatives from the Soka Gakkai organization in Hong Kong also rode the train with them, and the journey began amid pleasant conversation. On their way, they passed the Chinese University of Hong Kong that Shin'ichi had visited in January of 1974. Bright red blossoms were flowering against the fresh green leaves of the royal poinciana trees. The Hong Kong members were able to ride with Shin'ichi as far as Sheung Shui Station, one before Lo Wu Station, where they said their goodbyes.

A S SHIN'ICHI walked with Mineko from Lo Wu Station to Shenzhen Station, he said: "No doubt Kenzo Matsumura traveled this same route by wheelchair when he visited China four years ago. He was eighty-seven at the time. It was because Mr. Matsumura communicated my thoughts and ideas in detail to Premier Zhou that the premier has shown such consideration to the Clean Government Party. I'm very grateful.

"I consider myself to be carrying on where Mr. Matsumura left off in opening the path of Japan–China friendship. I will take great care not to betray the trust he placed in me and will dedicate myself wholeheartedly to building a bridge of mutual respect and friendship." Mineko smiled and nodded.

Looking up at the sky, Shin'ichi added: "I'm sure that Mr. Toda is also very happy about my visit. He hoped for the peace of Asia and the happiness of its people throughout his life."

"That's right," Mineko replied. "I can well imagine Mr. Toda smiling at this development."

Shin'ichi and Mineko conversed pleasantly, but the other members in their party were silent and looked rather glum. They were feeling tense about this first visit to China, a communist nation. That was probably only to be expected. The Cultural Revolution was still under way in China, and in Japan the news reported of scholars and artists being dragged through the streets wearing dunce caps and forced to engage in self-criticism. As a result, an image of China as a frightening place had been deeply impressed in the minds of the delegation members.

Shin'ichi smiled and said to them: "You should put on happy faces. We're on our way to make many new friends, aren't we? People are the same all over the world. The important thing is to be sincere and honest. Dialogue will definitely open the way to mutual understanding and empathy."

The British author H. G. Wells (1866–1946) declared, "Our true nationality is mankind."[5] This accords with the idea of global citizenship that Josei Toda articulated.

The proof of true humanism lies in having a warm smile for all people and the conviction that we are all fellow human beings with the ability to understand and accept one another.

A SMALL STREAM ran between Lo Wu and Shenzhen stations, marking the border between China and the British territory of Hong Kong. After crossing a steel bridge resembling an airplane hangar over the stream, Shin'ichi and his party came upon a couple of Chinese People's Liberation Army soldiers clad in khaki uniforms. They showed the soldiers their passports.

Shin'ichi had taken his first step on Chinese soil. It was 11:50 AM.

"Hello!" called out a voice in Japanese as a young man and two young women came running up to Shin'ichi and the others.

The young man and one of the young women were members of the China-Japan Friendship Association, while the other young woman worked for Guangzhou City, the capital of Guangdong Province. They were all bright and cheerful. They greeted Shin'ichi and the other members of the delegation with warm smiles and handshakes. The young man and woman from the China-Japan Friendship Association were named Ye Qiyong and Yin Lianyu, respectively. Mr. Ye said in fluent Japanese: "Welcome to China. We came from Beijing to act as your guides."

Shin'ichi's group and their Chinese guides enjoyed a pleasant conversation in the waiting room of Shenzhen Station. Mr. Ye had visited Japan seven times. He was a warmhearted person who had a smile for everyone. Ms.

Yin had studied Japanese at the Beijing Foreign Languages Institute (present-day Beijing Foreign Studies University). Her eyes shone brightly.

Mr. Ye said that he had greatly enjoyed reading Shin'ichi's novel *The Human Revolution*. As if confirming what he had read with Shin'ichi, he observed that the Soka Gakkai had struggled against the forces of fascism in Japan and that its first two presidents had been imprisoned and persecuted by the militarist government. Ms. Yin added that she knew the theme of *The Human Revolution*, and she proceeded to recite the passage "A great human revolution in just a single individual...."

"That's amazing!" Shin'ichi exclaimed. "I'm the author, and even I don't remember that!" Everyone laughed at Shin'ichi's humor. As the other members of the Japanese delegation watched Shin'ichi interact with their Chinese hosts, their image of China as a scary place disappeared.

The brightness and optimism of youth sends a refreshing breeze of hope into others' hearts. People make all the difference in the way a country or an organization is perceived.

L EARNING THAT Ye Qiyong and Yin Lianyu had read his novel *The Human Revolution*, Shin'ichi said with deep appreciation: "Thank you for reading my novel. As it illustrates, the Soka Gakkai has consistently striven to protect peace. The starting point of all our activities is to build a lasting, indestructible foundation for peace and friendship and to work for the happiness of all people."

The group boarded a train at Shenzhen Station heading for Guangzhou, where they were to transfer to a flight to Beijing. As they rode along, the Japanese delegation enjoyed a lively conversation with the China-Japan Friendship Association representatives. Shin'ichi asked many questions, ranging from the names of the trees and flowers passing by outside the windows to the history and special characteristics of China's main cities.

The renowned twelfth-century Confucian scholar Zhu Xi observed that one should never put off learning tomorrow what one can learn today. In that spirit, Shin'ichi always strove to learn and absorb as much as possible every moment. When we lose the desire to improve ourselves, we stop growing and stagnate.

Shortly before three in the afternoon, the group arrived at the station at Guangzhou, the capital of Guangdong Province. Several members of the Guangdong Province

Sub-Council of the Chinese People's Association for Friendship with Foreign Countries, including the vice president and the secretary-general, were waiting for them on the station platform.

"*Ni hao!*" said Shin'ichi, greeting them in Chinese. "Thank you for coming to welcome us. It's an honor to meet you. I thank you from the bottom of my heart." He then smiled and shook hands with the officials, who smiled warmly in return. Though this was their first encounter, the atmosphere was as comfortable as if they were old friends.

Noticing four women sitting in the station's waiting room, Shin'ichi went over to greet them, saying: "How do you do? We've come from Japan to promote friendship between our country and yours."

At first the women seemed taken aback, but soon they smiled and replied: "You've come all the way from Japan? Welcome!"

Observing this, the delegation members must have thought that they are all just human beings, all neighbors worthy of one another's respect.

FROM GUANGZHOU Station, Shin'ichi and his party were shown to the Guangdong Guest House. There they ate and talked with their hosts about cultural activities in Guangzhou, Chinese cuisine and various other subjects, getting to know one another and having an enjoyable time.

During the meal, the Guangdong Province Sub-Council secretary-general encouraged his guests to try a meat dish. It was very tender, light and delicious. The secretary-general asked with a smile: "Do you know what meat this is?"

"Is it chicken?" ventured a member of the Japanese delegation.

"No, it's frog," the secretary-general answered.

It was the first time any of the Japanese had eaten frog, and they looked surprised.

Grinning, the secretary-general added: "Guangdong is the food capital of China. The local cuisine is delicious and uses many different ingredients. In Guangdong, we eat anything. We eat anything that flies except airplanes, anything that swims except boats, and anything with four legs except tables and chairs."

The group burst into laughter.

Shin'ichi then remarked: "China's a big country, so it's not surprising that even its humor is big. You've managed to swallow the sky, the ocean and the earth in your description."

Once again everyone laughed heartily. As the Japanese delegation members looked on, they were reminded of Shin'ichi's earlier words that it was important to be sincere and honest in making new friends. Such sincere humanity is also the key to successful diplomacy.

After the banquet, the Japanese delegation went to the airport. Their plane left Guangzhou Airport at seven o'clock and arrived in Beijing at almost ten. Outside the airport, the Chinese characters *Beijing* shone in bright red neon lights. While waiting for the announcement to disembark, Shin'ichi gazed out the window. He saw a dozen or so individuals approaching the stairs leading up to the aircraft. They seemed to be coming to welcome them.

"I feel terrible that they should have to come here at such a late hour," Shin'ichi thought as he went down the stairs. At the head of the group waiting below stood President Liao Chengzhi of the China-Japan Friendship Association, his face wreathed in a warm smile.

PRESIDENT LIAO Chengzhi of the China-Japan Friendship Association was a stout man who exuded quiet dignity. With a kind smile, he addressed Shin'ichi in fluent Japanese: *"Yokoso, oide kuasaimashita!"* (Welcome, thank you for coming!) As he had been born in Japan, his Japanese was excellent.

"Thank you for coming here to the airport to greet us," Shin'ichi said. "And please allow me to express my deepest gratitude for arranging our invitation to China."

Shin'ichi firmly shook President Liao's plump hand, the warmth of which communicated his host's deep commitment to bilateral friendship. The others in the welcome party were top officials of the association. Shin'ichi shook hands with each of them in turn: Jing Puchun, council member and the wife of President Liao Chengzhi; Zhang Xiangshan, vice president; Zhao Puchu, vice president and also a Standing Committee member of the Chinese People's Political Consultative Conference; Sun Pinghua, secretary-general; and Jin Sucheng, council member. Shin'ichi couldn't help but interpret this sincere welcome as an indication of the strong wish of the Chinese for friendly relations between their two countries.

They were taken by car from the airport to their lodgings at the Beijing Hotel. Secretary-General Sun Pinghua rode alongside Shin'ichi. Speaking of the current situation in China, Mr. Sun said quietly, "China is still a poor country." It was a humble remark to make. At the same time, the word *still* conveyed a pride and determination to build a brighter future for China. In fact, he seemed to be filled with confidence and assurance in this prospect. Shin'ichi was also convinced that China would develop enormously in the future.

Though a country may presently enjoy wealth, if its people lack the desire to contribute to its future prosperity, decline will lie ahead. But a country can lose sight of this important point if it becomes intoxicated by its own wealth and arrogant about its success. Nichiren Daishonin writes, "A wise person, while dwelling in security, anticipates danger; a perverse one, while dwelling amid danger, takes security for granted" (WND-1, 621).

Prosperity and decline are not caused by the times; they are the result of the attitudes and actions of the people.

WHEN SHIN'ICHI ARRIVED at the Beijing Hotel, there was a group of Japanese journalists waiting to interview him. He had traveled very far that day, from Hong Kong to Guangzhou, and then from there to Beijing. It was late, and the other members of his party wanted Shin'ichi, who had been going at full speed all day, to get to bed as quickly as possible. But Shin'ichi gladly agreed to be interviewed. He wished to take every possible opportunity to assert the importance of friendly Japan–China relations, for the sake of the future of both nations and for world peace.

As Shin'ichi began speaking, he felt a surge of strength. His passion for his convictions swept away his exhaustion and fresh resolve rose within him.

By the time Shin'ichi and the others went up to their hotel rooms, unpacked and finished another brief meeting, it was past midnight Beijing time.

The next morning, May 31, the streets of the city were filled with people riding bicycles to work and school. It was a vibrant scene overflowing with the energy of the people. Members of the China-Japan Friendship Association, including council member Jin Sucheng, drove Shin'ichi and his party to the Forbidden City, or Palace Museum, a vast imperial palace complex from the Ming and Qing dynasties located in the center of Beijing. The entrance to the Forbidden City was called Tiananmen, or the Gate of Heavenly Peace, and the square and streets in front of it were said to be large enough for a million people to gather. Mao Zedong proclaimed the establishment of the People's Republic of China from atop this gate on October 1, 1949.

Shin'ichi and the others stepped out of the car at the main entrance to the Forbidden City. They crossed a bridge, walked through the Gate of Supreme Harmony and stopped in front of the Hall of Supreme Harmony. Said to be the largest wooden structure in China, it was an important ceremonial site that had once been used for celebrating imperial enthronements, birthdays and other occasions.

A wonderful carving of a dragon stood out in relief on a large stone slab next to the staircase leading to the Hall of Preserving Harmony, which was behind the Hall of Supreme Harmony. Known as the Dragon-in-the-Clouds Staircase, it had been reserved for the emperor's exclusive use. The stone slab bearing the carving had come from Fangshan, about thirty-one miles southwest of Beijing. Weighing some two hundred fifty tons, it was nearly fifty-five feet long and ten feet wide. It had been brought to the palace in Beijing in the winter by covering the roads with water, which froze, and then rolling the slab to the capital on large wooden logs.

THE FORBIDDEN CITY occupied about 178 acres and had some nine thousand rooms. More than a million workers, including those who mined the stones and cut the timber to build the palace, were said to have been involved in its fourteen-year construction. All of the buildings were ornately crafted, conveying a feeling of the enormous power wielded by the Chinese emperor.

Shin'ichi's guide pointed to a building in the distance and remarked: "That's where the meals of Empress Dowager Cixi, the consort of the Qing-dynasty Xianfeng Emperor, were prepared. Some four hundred fifty cooks and kitchen workers were employed just to fix her daily meals."

"I wonder what they could have been making that so many people were required," mused Shin'ichi.

"An inordinate number of dishes were prepared, but she only ate a few," the guide explained. "She enjoyed the smell of the food being cooked more than eating it. It is said that the cost of a single meal prepared for her was enough to feed five thousand peasants for a day."

This was truly a sign of the extreme arrogance of the powerful. Shin'ichi was reminded of the famous words of British historian Lord Acton (1834–1902): "Power tends to corrupt and absolute power corrupts absolutely."[6]

The common people, on the other hand, lacking enough food to eat, were suffering from starvation. It is no surprise that they eventually rose up in revolt, in spite of the authorities' efforts to keep them down. Through their victory, the once "Forbidden City" was turned into a museum open to the people.

Chinese premier Zhou Enlai (1898–1976) observed, "The people have always been the incarnation of justice."[7] It is an unchanging rule of history that government authorities who scorn the people and trample on their rights while indulging in luxury and excess themselves are destined to fall in the end. *The Essentials of Government in the Chen-kuan Era*, a Chinese classic on the art of leadership, declares that the people are the foundation of the realm.[8] This is an eternal truth. Any nation that ignores the welfare of the people, its foundation, will be destroyed.

The Soka Gakkai's strength lies in the fact that it has brought together and organized ordinary people, expanded that network and enabled each person to tap their full potential. Each person has subsequently gone out and contributed in their unique way to the betterment of society and the actualization of justice. This is what had attracted Premier Zhou Enlai to the Soka Gakkai and why he trusted the organization so deeply.

IN THE AFTERNOON, Shin'ichi and his party visited the Xinhua Elementary School and its attached kindergarten in Xicheng District, Beijing. Both Shin'ichi and Mineko were overjoyed to have this opportunity. They were eager to see the faces of the Chinese children, to learn what they cared about and how their daily lives were.

To interact with children is to interact with the future.

To foster children is to foster the future.

Shin'ichi's main purpose on this trip to China was to promote educational exchange. He knew that the only way to establish lasting friendship between Japan and China was to broadly open the way for interaction among the younger generations of both nations.

The students and teachers of the Xinhua Elementary School warmly welcomed the visitors. Meeting with the teaching staff in one of the rooms on campus, Shin'ichi expressed his gratitude for their heartfelt welcome and spoke about the history of the Soka Gakkai and its involvement in education. He said: "The Soka Gakkai started out as a group of teachers, the Soka Kyoiku Gakkai (Value-creating Education Society). The organization's first and second presidents, Tsunesaburo Makiguchi and Josei Toda, were both educators. Mr. Makiguchi strongly believed that the purpose of education was to enable children to live happy lives, and he developed his theory of value-creating education in order to realize that goal.

"Both men, however—men who fought for the happiness of ordinary people—were imprisoned by the militarist authorities ruling Japan during the World War II, and Mr. Makiguchi died in prison for his beliefs. My mentor, Mr. Toda, inherited and carried on Mr. Makiguchi's vision." Shin'ichi was always proudest when he talked about the path of mentor and disciple of the Soka Gakkai.

The Xinhua Elementary School faculty listened actively and intently as Shin'ichi spoke.

The struggles of the first two Soka Gakkai presidents are a shining example of the universal struggle for human justice. Therefore, when we share the Soka Gakkai's history with people from other countries, they can readily grasp the principles and ideals that our organization is based on.

Shin'ichi continued, his heart filled with gratitude for the first two presidents, "I learned of Mr. Makiguchi's educational thought and philosophy from Mr. Toda, and went on to found schools in which those ideas are put into practice."

"THERE ARE FIVE Soka schools in Japan—a boys' junior high school and high school in Tokyo, a girls' junior high school and high school in Osaka, and a university in Tokyo.[9] We are also making preparations to establish an elementary school. That's why I would like to learn as much as possible from your school today."

A faculty representative responded: "We're honored that you've come to see our school. Your visit is a great encouragement to all of us—teachers and students alike. It is also, in my opinion, a significant opportunity for us in terms of deepening understanding between our countries and considering the future of education."

Smiling, Shin'ichi asserted: "Thinking of the twenty-first century, I believe that education is a subject of prime importance. That is because education plays a crucial role in enriching human culture and creating a peaceful society. Unfortunately, in many ways, education has reached an impasse both in Japan and around the world. The time has come for educational reform."

The faculty members listened intently as he spoke. One of the teachers then began to explain with enthusiasm the history of the Xinhua Elementary School and Chinese educational policies in general: "We have more than one thousand children here in twenty-six classes. In China today, elementary school education has been reduced from six years to five. It has been shortened by one year, but children study the same amount in five years that they used to in six."

Shin'ichi was most impressed by the fact that the teachers were seeking to implement the kind of education that would inspire students and enhance their awareness. The teaching staff also said that they aimed to achieve a balance among intellectual, moral and physical education. Toward this end, in addition to their general courses, students in the upper grades of elementary school took a course on ethics and morality in an effort to prepare them for society.

After the establishment of the People's Republic of China in 1949, education was provided widely to workers and farmers, and this served as a powerful driving force for China's growth and development.

The teachers' voices were filled with pride and a sense of the importance of their mission as educators. Such pride and conviction are the greatest sources of power in fostering people.

THE TEACHER continued: "We try to encourage and guide the children to have a vision for their future and to pursue their goals. We also devote considerable energy to helping them realize the importance of serving the people." Further explaining that the school strove to combine education with productive labor, the teacher asserted: "People need to know how to use a ruler and a scale, for example. What good is arithmetic if you cannot measure a plot of land? An education that doesn't teach children the difference between corn and millet is worthless."

Shin'ichi nodded as he listened. "Yes, that's very true. Your comments are very helpful. You've brought up some points that Japanese education should consider as well."

Interacting with these passionately committed educators gave Shin'ichi great hope for China's future. The French author Victor Hugo (1802–85) wrote, "The future lies in the hand of the schoolmaster."[10]

Shin'ichi and his party visited several classrooms and observed the classes in progress. When Shin'ichi greeted the students warmly in Chinese, they responded with enthusiasm. He then said to them, "For the sake of people around the world, please study hard and grow up to

be bright and strong young people." The children nodded shyly in response.

The school also operated a small factory that produced Chinese chessboards. Through helping out at the factory, the children learned the importance of working hard and were able to put their school lessons to practical use. A retired factory technician supervised the operation.

While it's critical that labor not deprive students of time to study and decrease their scholastic ability, it can also be a significant part of education. Observing the students joyously at work in the factory, Shin'ichi smiled and said to himself, *How happy Mr. Makiguchi would be to see this!*

From the late 1800s on, first Soka Gakkai president Tsunesaburo Makiguchi had proposed a half-day school system, in which students would spend half the day engaging in formal study and the other half engaging in productive labor, thereby achieving both intellectual and physical growth.

AFTER OBSERVING the classrooms, Shin'ichi and his party spoke again with the teaching staff. Shin'ichi peppered them with questions: "What kind of education are you encouraging families to undertake at home?" "How do you motivate students to develop their unique personalities?" "What do you regard as the right age to begin foreign language training?" Shin'ichi was determined to take every opportunity to learn whatever he could from those he encountered. He, therefore, always had an unending stream of questions ready. Asking questions is an expression of the desire for continual self-improvement and learning.

The teachers confidently answered Shin'ichi's questions. He also asked them: "Earlier you said that you conducted political and ideological education. How do you do that?"

One of the teachers replied: "We have a course on politics, which is the main way we approach those subjects. Our teaching methods differ according to the students' ages, but our emphasis is on studying the Chinese revolutionary spirit and transmitting the importance of serving the people. Studying such heroes as Lei Feng is one way we communicate this message."

Lei Feng was born to a poor farming family and lost his parents at an early age. With the establishment of the People's Republic of China, he enrolled in school and eventually joined the People's Liberation Army. He performed numerous virtuous acts and came to be admired as a model soldier. He died in an accident while on duty at the young age of twenty-two.

An ideology is best taught through the example of individuals who embody it. It is people's lives that reveal the value of an ideology.

Shin'ichi inquired further, "What steps are you taking to enable children to gain an objective perspective of their nation's government?"

Another teacher responded: "Through studying current events, we give them the opportunity to learn about the governments of other nations, and we also teach them about the difference between the government of China before and after the revolution. In addition, rather than merely lecturing, we try to hold discussions among the students to enable them to make the ideology we are teaching their own."

An ideology that is forced on people will never take root in their hearts. One of the critical points of education is to encourage children to foster the ability to think for themselves and make their own judgments.

THE PATH of education is long, and its results only really become clear thirty or fifty years later.

The Chinese teachers were filled with confidence that the education they were giving their students would bear wonderful fruit in the future. At the time, the vast nation of China had a population of eight hundred million. Ensuring that all of its youth had equal access to education was in itself an enormous task. The teachers were proud of the new China that was making this a reality.

As their visit came to a close, Shin'ichi and his party thanked the Xinhua Elementary School teachers. Bidding their hosts farewell, they continued on with their itinerary.

Shortly after five that afternoon, Shin'ichi and his party visited the China-Japan Friendship Association. Shin'ichi wished to express once again his gratitude for the invitation to China and the gracious welcome they had received.

Association President Liao Chengzhi greeted them with a warm smile. Shin'ichi reiterated his appreciation for his coming to meet them at the airport the night before. After they sat for a photo to commemorate the occasion, a friendly discussion ensued.

When Shin'ichi shared the Soka Gakkai's history of fighting against severe opposition, President Liao replied brightly: "Facing challenges like that is rewarding. It makes you stronger." These words of President Liao, who himself had surmounted all manner of difficulties, carried great weight.

Born in Tokyo in 1908, Liao Chengzhi had lived a turbulent life. His father was Liao Zhongkai, a revolutionary leader who worked closely with Sun Yat-sen, known as the father of modern China, and his mother He Xiangning was also an active member of the Chinese Revolutionary League. His parents had fled to Japan along with Sun Yat-sen, who frequently visited their home and held meetings there. Photographs from the period show Liao Chengzhi as a boy sitting on Sun Yat-sen's lap.

In those days, many Japanese arrogantly viewed their fellow Asians with contempt. Liao Chengzhi had even been called a "little pig" by a teacher at school. But growing up in a family filled with revolutionary spirit, he redirected all his frustrations toward the struggle to liberate his homeland.

No life is free from troubles. Only by boldly facing the winds of adversity can one soar into the skies of victory, joy and genuine fulfillment.

EVENTUALLY, Liao Chengzhi returned with his parents to China. The summer that Mr. Liao was sixteen years old, his father was assassinated in Guangzhou by political enemies. He died right before his wife's eyes. Mr. Liao's stouthearted mother hung a banner across the entrance to their house reading, "The Spirit Never Dies." It was a stirring declaration by a proud and valiant woman.

A woman's firm determination gives her invincible strength to achieve her goals.

Liao Chengzhi inherited his parents' revolutionary

spirit. He was persecuted, and was arrested seven times as a result. During the Long March, he was accused of being a spy and forced to march in handcuffs. And during the Cultural Revolution, he was the target of unwarranted attacks and placed under confinement for four years, from 1967 to 1971. He was forbidden contact with anyone except for a weekly visit from his wife. Though he suffered from a heart condition, he was denied medical treatment. Throughout this time, he was protected by Chinese Premier Zhou Enlai.

Liao Chengzhi wrote, "The greatest lesson I've learned is that strong convictions make one invulnerable to one's enemies."[11] The arduous trials he had experienced had forged in him unshakable conviction.

The conversation flowed vibrantly between Shin'ichi and Liao Chengzhi, two men who were prepared to give their very lives in the struggle to realize happiness for the people. It resonated with a beautiful bond of friendship forged by shared commitment. As they spoke, Shin'ichi expressed his wish to promote educational and cultural exchange by making a donation of five thousand books to the library of Peking University and inviting Chinese youth and students to visit Japan.

Afterward, the group moved to the Beijing Hotel for a welcome banquet hosted by the China-Japan Friendship Association. It was attended by Association President Liao Chengzhi and his wife, Jing Puchun; vice presidents Zhang Xiangshan and Zhao Puchu; Secretary-General Sun Pinghua; council members Jin Sucheng and Lin Liyun; and Japan-China Cultural Exchange Association Permanent Director Kinkazu Saionji and his wife, as well as their son Kazuteru Saionji, a journalist who had studied at Peking University.

In his opening remarks, President Liao extended a warm welcome to the Soka Gakkai delegation and declared that China–Japan friendship was a powerful historical current that no force could obstruct.

PRESIDENT LIAO then mentioned the proposal for the normalization of diplomatic relations between Japan and China that Shin'ichi had made at the Soka Gakkai's 11th Student Division General Meeting in 1968. President Liao spoke with emphasis, as if to reaffirm the proposal's content: "We both laud and admire President Yamamoto's clear foresight and positive attitude toward the issue of China–Japan relations." He concluded his remarks by saying that he hoped to further promote bilateral friendship.

Shin'ichi responded by expressing his sincere gratitude for the warm welcome his delegation had received. He then said: "The Soka Gakkai may still be a small and inexperienced organization, but I hope you can see that we have a great passion for promoting peace and friendly relations. While treasuring the golden bridge of friendship built by our predecessors, I am resolved to dedicate my life to earnestly working to expand and strengthen that bridge so that it will endure for generations to come."

A convivial discussion ensued over dinner. President Liao asked each member of the Japanese delegation about his or her impressions of China. He also asked Mineko. She demurred, however, thinking of her role as being primarily a behind-the-scenes support to the group. The

Chinese hosts nevertheless continued to press her good-naturedly to share her opinion.

She finally conceded, and said: "Since you insist, I'll share my honest impression with you. In Japan, people are afraid of Communism. To tell you the truth, I also had a fearful image of your country."

Shin'ichi looked at Mineko, wondering what she might say next.

She smiled and continued without hesitation, "But having this opportunity to speak with the Chinese people directly, I have come to see that it is a very warmhearted and humanistic country."

Everyone applauded. President Liao said: "You have spoken truthfully and honestly. That's the way to make friends!"

Mineko's words brought everyone in the room closer together. Friendship deepens when people speak sincerely and honestly to one another.

DURING THEIR discussions, President Liao Chengzhi remarked casually to Shin'ichi, "President Yamamoto, you can promote the teachings upheld by the Soka Gakkai here in China if you like."

Shin'ichi replied firmly, but with a smile: "That's not necessary. China is currently advancing along a path of construction following the ideology of Maoism. If that brings happiness to the people, then the goal of Buddhism will also be fulfilled. All that matters is that your nation continues to enjoy peace and prosperity."

Shin'ichi did not go to China with the aim of propagating Nichiren Buddhism. He had gone there as a humanitarian committed to realizing peace, and his purpose was to open a lasting path of friendship. He had no desire for any sort of special favor to be extended to the Soka Gakkai in exchange—a fact he wished to make perfectly clear to his hosts.

Shin'ichi also believed that if, through sincere and open dialogue, Chinese leaders came to appreciate the principles of compassion and the sanctity of life articulated by Nichiren Buddhism, they would come to be reflected in all aspects of Chinese society without actually spreading the teaching. After all, both the principles of "three thousand realms in a single moment of life" and "the oneness of life and its environment" had originated in China.

The following day, June 1, was Children's Day in China. Shin'ichi and his party had been invited to a celebration of the holiday at the Working People's Cultural Palace in Beijing, to the east of Tiananmen Gate. Some fifty thousand people would be participating in the festival. There were song and dance performances, magic and puppet shows, exhibits and games. Happy voices reverberated across the spacious site.

In the area where the music and dance performances were taking place, a bright-eyed girl with a yellow ribbon in her hair took Shin'ichi by the hand and led him to his seat. Bashfully, she asked him, "Where are you from?"

"I'm from Japan," Shin'ichi replied. "I came all this way just to meet you."

The girl smiled. Shin'ichi treasured every encounter, whether it was with an adult or a child, and he spoke to each person with an earnest wish to make friends.

The path of friendship is opened broadly when we

strive with sincerity and wisdom to make the most of every encounter.

SHIN'ICHI ASKED the girl, "What do you want to be when you grow up?"

"I'll do anything I can to help the people," she said.

Shin'ichi was impressed. She had clearly been taught the importance of working for others.

Education that teaches the value of contributing to society and one's fellow human beings can be called humanistic. *If all children shared this spirit*, Shin'ichi thought, *they could build a truly wonderful society.*

Shin'ichi had a Polaroid photo taken of him and the girl and gave it to her. She smiled happily, thanking him over and over.

As Shin'ichi and the others walked through the area, they heard people cheering and shouting, "*Jiayou! Jiayou!*" (Go! Go!). They had come upon a tricycle race. Shin'ichi joined in shouting "*Jiayou!*" with the other spectators to cheer on the contestants.

The race finished and prizes were presented to the winners.

One of the children sitting near Shin'ichi playfully mimed taking a photo of the scene, stirring laughter among the crowd. Shin'ichi in turn had the *Seikyo Shimbun* photographer traveling with him take a Polaroid photo of the boy as he did so.

"We caught you in the act!" Shin'ichi said jokingly. When this was translated, the boy and a group of children gathered around eagerly to see how the instant photo would turn out. When the image appeared, they all cheered.

"I'm going to officially present you with this now," Shin'ichi said to the boy. "I offer you this photograph in the name of China–Japan friendship."

The boy accepted it respectfully and declared in a clear voice: "Thank you very much. We'll all work hard for China–Japan friendship, too!" His words were greeted with applause and warmhearted laughter by the surrounding spectators.

SHIN'ICHI WAS reminded of a passage the Chinese writer Lu Xun had penned in the 1930s about a group of children in Shanghai: "On the main roads, however, your eyes are caught by the splendid, lively foreign children playing or walking—you see scarcely any Chinese children at all. Not that there are none, but with their tattered clothes and lackluster expression they pale into insignificance beside the others."[12] Lu Xun went on to warn that those very children were the image of China's future.

But the Chinese children whom Shin'ichi saw now were bright and energetic, their faces shining with hope. Just a little more than two decades since the establishment of the People's Republic of China, education had been extended to everyone, and great importance was placed on children, who were encouraged to grow freely and confidently. People's basic needs for food, clothing and shelter were met, and the overall consensus was that their lives were definitely better than they had been prior to the revolution.

The actual feelings of the people are the foundation upon which government rests; a government that becomes divorced from the people will lose their support.

Shin'ichi prayed sincerely that the children he met would enjoy happy, hope-filled lives.

A meeting with representatives of the China-Japan Friendship Association took place at the Beijing Hotel from three on the afternoon of June 1. Association Vice President Zhang Xiangshan, Secretary-General Sun Pinghua, and council members Lin Liyun and Jin Sucheng attended, with Huang Shiming acting as interpreter. The meeting lasted for three hours and was followed by another three-hour conference on the morning of June 3. Many different subjects were discussed, including the international situation, Japan–China relations, the nature of war and issues related to peace. It was a very meaningful exchange in which members of both delegations frankly shared their opinions about the complicated topics.

The Chinese viewed the world as being in a state of dramatic flux. Shin'ichi also believed that it was a time of great changes and, on the most fundamental level, he shared the perspective of his counterparts. The two sides agreed that there was a danger of a third world war breaking out and that earnest efforts needed to be made for peace in order to avoid such a catastrophe. The Chinese expressed the opinion that the major potential cause for war was tensions between the two superpowers, the United States and the Soviet Union.

SHIN'ICHI STRESSED the need for people to look deep within themselves to find the root cause of war. He argued that war's most fundamental source is the egoism, arrogance and demonic nature of power lying in the depths of people's lives and the mutual distrust and fear produced as a result.

The Chinese hosts also expressed concern about a revival of militarism in Japan. Shin'ichi and his party pointed to spiritual emptiness and apathy as the breeding ground for the emergence of fascism.

The aim of the movement carried out by the Soka Gakkai is to give people wisdom and strength. This is true empowerment of the people.

Shin'ichi's biggest concern, and the topic he most wished to discuss, was the discord between China and the Soviet Union. The border between the two countries was rife with tension, and it seemed that the slightest incident might trigger open hostilities.

Both China and the Soviet Union were socialist nations subscribing to the teachings of Marx and Lenin. With the world divided between the capitalist and communist camps, they had enjoyed strong relations and cooperated on numerous international issues. But in 1956, the situation changed when the two countries came into conflict. In February of that year, at the 20th Congress of the Communist Party of the Soviet Union, First Secretary Nikita Khrushchev announced a new policy of peaceful coexistence with the capitalist powers. He publicly criticized former General Secretary Joseph Stalin, who had died three years earlier, denouncing his dictatorship and the brutal purges he had conducted. Not only did he condemn Joseph Stalin, whose influence as a communist leader reached beyond the Soviet Union, but he also announced a new direction in socialism. His declaration sent shock waves through the communist world.

Chinese leaders, who had adopted a policy of opposing "U.S. imperialism," were suspicious of the sudden shift signaled by Mr. Khrushchev and expressed their disagreement with it. This was the start of a schism between the two nations. In April 1960, China officially criticized the new Soviet party line in its publication *Hongqi* (Red Flag). The Soviet Union responded to this criticism. The situation intensified with the Chinese calling Mr. Khrushchev and the Soviet leaders revisionists, and the Soviets accusing Mao Zedong and the Chinese leadership of dogmatism.

IN JULY 1960, the Soviet Union decided to withdraw the more than one thousand engineers it had sent to China as well as to cease providing the country with foreign aid. China had depended heavily on the subsidies it received from the Soviet Union, so this move was a great shock to Chinese economic policy.

In October 1964, China succeeded in testing its first atomic weapon. Then, in 1966, the Chinese Cultural Revolution began. The Soviet Union harshly criticized this movement as a grave error deriving from Maoism.

In 1968, the Soviet Union together with the armies of four other communist states invaded the socialist republic of Czechoslovakia to suppress a people's movement for democracy. Witnessing this military intervention, China felt threatened by the Soviet Union and began to wonder if it might be the next target of Soviet aggression.

In March 1969, fighting broke out between Chinese and Soviet border police over the ownership of Zhenbao Island in the Wusuli River—or Damanski Island on the Ussuri River, as the Soviets regarded it. In July, Chinese and Soviet forces also exchanged fire over Pacha Island in the Heilong River (Goldinski Island in the Amur River, according to Soviet geography). The Chinese felt very threatened, and tensions between the two nations escalated.

People in Beijing began to dig underground bomb shelters. At the same time, the Chinese government attempted to improve diplomatic relations with the United States, which it had formerly denounced as imperialist, in an effort to offset the perceived Soviet threat.

In 1971, China was admitted into the United Nations and, in 1972, relations between Japan and China were normalized, but Chinese–Soviet relations continued to deteriorate. China labeled the Soviet Union as "socialist imperialists" and regarded the country as its foremost enemy.

Shin'ichi's greatest fear was that war might break out between the two nations, both of which possessed nuclear weapons, and he strongly felt that it must be prevented at all costs. He was determined to do anything in his power to ensure this. He had faith in the power of dialogue. As a Buddhist, he believed in people. He was certain that through dialogue, people's conscience could be touched and war could be avoided.

IN MARCH 1974, immediately prior to Shin'ichi's visit to China, China arrested the crew of a Soviet helicopter that had invaded Chinese air space and accused the Soviet Union of spying. The situation had reached such a degree of tension that war might break out at any moment.

The French historian Jules Michelet (1798–1874)

stressed the importance of acting without pretense and speaking frankly, as one human being to another.[13]

Shin'ichi frankly remarked to China-Japan Friendship Association Vice President Zhang Xiangshan: "I lost my eldest brother in war, and my home was burned down in bombing raids. I am completely and utterly opposed to war. I must ask you, will China ever invade another country?"

Vice President Zhang asserted: "Chinese history has been one of invasion and attack from other nations. We know only too well how important national independence is and how miserable it is to be invaded. As such, I believe that China will never invade another country."

Shin'ichi felt that this reply was very significant. The Chinese knew that Shin'ichi would be visiting the Soviet Union in the fall. This might well have been a message that they wished Shin'ichi would deliver to the Soviet Union. But Shin'ichi had no intention of trying to decipher the political motives or intentions of other nations. He simply accepted the words at face value and bore them in mind. The Chinese had no intention of launching an invasion. This meant there was a chance that a military confrontation between China and the Soviet Union could be avoided. Shin'ichi was very glad to hear these words. He felt that they were one positive result of the frank dialogue that is a part of human diplomacy.

Naturally, the topic of nuclear weapons came up in the two meetings between Shin'ichi's delegation and the China-Japan Friendship Association members.

After successfully testing a nuclear weapon in 1964, China joined the United States, the Soviet Union, the United Kingdom and France as the fifth nuclear power.

Emphasizing the supreme value of life and human existence from his perspective as a Buddhist, Shin'ichi strongly conveyed his wish for the complete elimination of nuclear weapons, declaring that all nuclear testing, weapons production and stockpiling must be stopped toward that end. This was the injunction that second Soka Gakkai president Josei Toda had imparted to Shin'ichi and the other youth of the Soka Gakkai.

THE GLOBAL nuclear arms race was heating up. In May 1974, India conducted an underground nuclear test, and Pakistan also announced that it was developing nuclear weapons. Nuclear proliferation showed no signs of abating. Rather, the nuclear capabilities of the United States and the Soviet Union continued to increase year by year, turning the entire planet into a nuclear powder keg. In this context, Shin'ichi was utterly determined to create a movement for the eradication of nuclear weapons. He voiced this message at Soka Gakkai general meetings and any other opportunity he had.

Soka Gakkai youth division members stood up in response to Shin'ichi's call, starting a petition drive to collect ten million signatures demanding the elimination of nuclear arms and publishing collections of atomic bomb victims' experiences. Their efforts gave rise to a burgeoning antinuclear movement.

In speaking with China-Japan Friendship Association Vice President Zhang Xiangshan and his party, Shin'ichi strongly argued the need to eradicate nuclear weapons for the sake of humanity's future. Since China had chosen to develop nuclear weapons as a means of self-defense, Shin'ichi's hosts may have found his remarks rather unsettling. But they clearly stated that abolishing and eliminating nuclear weapons was in fact China's real intention. They went on to suggest that toward that end, all nuclear powers should sign an agreement stating that they would never employ nuclear weapons, and that the nuclear facilities and stockpiles those nations had in other countries should be removed.

Vice President Zhang remarked, "People cannot wear or eat nuclear weapons."

Shin'ichi felt as if these words expressed China's true thoughts on the subject. Yet China was continuing to conduct nuclear tests. When Shin'ichi inquired about this, Vice President Zhang replied: "Both the United States and the Soviet Union have huge nuclear stockpiles, and while calling for disarmament, they are actually increasing those arsenals. Given that reality, China has no choice but to continue nuclear testing and to possess nuclear armaments."

Shin'ichi stressed his wish that China would send out a strong message by courageously taking the first step and eliminating its nuclear weapons. This was because he knew that no matter how much a country called for nuclear abolition, as long as it possessed them, its words would mean nothing and a trend toward disarmament would not be launched.

Shin'ichi urged his counterparts to stand up and change the course of history.

VICE PRESIDENT ZHANG said, as if making a pledge: "Though we may continue to conduct nuclear tests, under no circumstances will China be the first to employ nuclear weapons. They are for defensive purposes only."

The Soka Gakkai delegation and their Chinese hosts had a difference of opinion in some respects regarding nuclear weapons. However, they agreed completely that all nations, whether or not they possessed such an arsenal, should gather in a single venue and hold a conference to explore nuclear abolition.

The conclusion of a peace and friendship treaty between Japan and China, which Shin'ichi had previously advocated in his novel *The Human Revolution* and on other occasions, also came up for discussion in the meetings. Shin'ichi suggested that in addition to signing a treaty, a crucial means to achieving genuine bilateral friendship was to promote exchange between the people of Japan and China.

It is, after all, people who make treaties effective. It is people who ultimately give meaning to the external formality of a treaty. It is people's spirit that makes such an agreement a reality. Peace and friendship will endure only when mutual trust and friendship is fostered between people. The ancient Roman philosopher Cicero said, "Place friendship above every other human concern that can be imagined!"[14]

The discussion with the members of the China-Japan Friendship Association grew impassioned. In a sense, it was a dialogue between China, a country that upheld Marxist-Leninist teachings denying the spirit of religion, and the Soka Gakkai, a religious organization based on Nichiren Buddhism. Many of Shin'ichi's traveling companions seemed to think that they would find little to agree upon with their Chinese hosts. To the contrary, however, they discovered many points of strong agreement through their talks—such as their opposition to fascism, the need to conclude a peace and friendship treaty between the two countries, and the importance of eliminating nuclear weapons.

Those who share a sincere concern for people's welfare and a wish for peace can transcend ideological barriers to reach a profound accord and understanding. This is because, irrespective of the social or political system of the country we live in, we are all human beings who share a desire for peace and the prosperity of our fellow citizens.

Through this experience, the young people in Shin'ichi's party deepened their conviction in the power of dialogue to realize peace, a point that Shin'ichi had been stressing to them for some time.

O N JUNE 2, the fourth day of his visit to China, Shin'ichi and his party visited a factory using semiconductors to manufacture precision machinery in Beijing's Xicheng District. Most of the approximately three hundred fifty employees at the factory were women. Prior to the establishment of the People's Republic of China, women were relegated to the shadows, unable to participate fully in society. After the revolution, however, under the slogan "Women Hold Up Half the Sky," the foundation for gender equality was solidly laid, and the social position of women improved dramatically.

According to the factory supervisor, the facility had previously been a small neighborhood business that

manufactured balancing scales, but it had been transformed through the painstaking efforts of the women
working there. When the factory shifted to producing
transistors in 1965, ten women employees were chosen to
study at Tsinghua University. They were barely literate at
the time, but their resolve to contribute to their nation's
growth was unrivaled by anyone.

One day during a class at the university, the women
were told to take a look at blueprints for a diffusion furnace used in the manufacturing of semiconductors. When
they opened the plans, some of the other students in the
class began to snicker derisively. "What's so funny?" they
asked—only to be told that they were viewing the blueprints upside down.

The women knew nothing at the start, but they worked

incredibly hard. They never gave up, and they succeeded in absorbing difficult information at a rapid pace. At times the effort gave them a headache, but they just took some aspirin and continued studying. A year later, they completed their first diffusion furnace.

The French philosopher Jean-Jacques Rousseau (1712–78) observed, "All peoples who have had morals have respected women."[15] Countries and organizations in which women are allowed to realize their full potential always grow and develop by leaps and bounds.

After listening to this account of the factory's history, Shin'ichi and the others were given a tour of the plant. They were introduced to one of the women who had attended Tsinghua University. Shin'ichi took a photo of her using a Polaroid camera and presented her with the finished print. He then remarked: "I was very moved by the story of your wonderful struggle. I would like to extol your efforts and achievements eternally."

The woman's face glowed with gratitude and pride.

IN THE AFTERNOON, Shin'ichi and his party visited a people's commune on the outskirts of Beijing. People's communes constituted a system that was adopted in some rural villages combining economic, governmental and political functions. The commune that Shin'ichi visited consisted of 26,686 acres on a 39,536-acre plot that was communally farmed by seventeen thousand families comprising a total of eighty thousand individuals.

The soil on the site was highly alkaline and in the past had been rather unproductive. There were also many low-lying areas that were susceptible to flooding. Under the old regime, those farming the land had lived a very hard life. But with the founding of the People's Republic of China in 1949, land reform was implemented, and people's communes were established, leading to a gradual increase in agricultural productivity.

The commune staff member guiding Shin'ichi and the others explained that in 1973, the rice yield was a little more than forty-six hundred pounds per acre—a seven-fold increase over the yield of about six hundred sixty pounds prior to the revolution. The commune also raised pigs and planted orchards in an attempt to diversify its agricultural production.

The guide further shared that the commune had also made great advances in the sphere of education, establishing elementary schools, junior high schools and other such facilities. Before 1949, he said, most children were unable to attend school and were illiterate, but today all children received an education and were given an opportunity to improve their scholastic ability.

"This is a major achievement," Shin'ichi remarked.

The commune representative replied: "I think our production output will be better than ever this year. But there are some areas in which we still have a lot to do. We need to keep making efforts toward development."

Shin'ichi asked, "Do you set a clear output target for each year?"

"Yes, we do," he responded. "I think our development thus far can be attributed to the fact that the Chinese people have united toward a common goal and worked hard to achieve it."

"That's a keen analysis," Shin'ichi said. "When people unite their efforts to realize a clear common goal based on high ideals, they can exhibit great strength. Without a goal, there can be no progress. The most important question is how to inspire people to give their all."

The foundation of any organization is its people. The will and enthusiasm of each individual is the driving force behind everything. Stagnation results when that is forgotten.

SHIN'ICHI NEXT visited the hospital in the people's commune. In addition, having expressed a wish to see people's homes to observe their way of life, he was able to speak with the families in person. Friendship between nations is but a pipe dream unless the hearts of the people of both countries are brought together. That is why Shin'ichi poured his energies into interacting with the Chinese people.

On June 3, after completing their second meeting with representatives of the China-Japan Friendship Association, Shin'ichi and his party visited Beijing No. 35 Junior High School. When they entered the school, they came upon a blackboard with the words "A Warm Welcome for Our Japanese Friends" written on it.

The group observed a class in session. Shin'ichi and Mineko sat among the students and listened to the teacher. Between classes, the students sang, danced, and played the piano, the accordion and the Chinese two-stringed fiddle. Shin'ichi then went to take a look at the room where the table tennis club practiced. Finding students practicing their sport, he asked if he could join them. When the interpreter communicated Shin'ichi's request, the students smiled with pleasure.

A girl in her third year of junior high school was chosen

to play against Shin'ichi. Shin'ichi had loved playing table tennis since he was a boy and, in fact, it was one of his better sports. But when the match began, the student quickly took the first point. She was very agile, returning the ball with astonishing speed. Halfway through the game, a member of the Japanese group handed Shin'ichi his favorite table tennis paddle, which Shin'ichi had brought with him from Japan. Shin'ichi tried his best to return his opponent's shots, but in the end, he was defeated by a close margin. "You're good!" he said. "I'm impressed." He shook the girl's hand, and she smiled brightly. As a gesture of thanks, he gave her his own paddle in honor of her victory.

As Shin'ichi was leaving the room, the girl ran up to him and held out a brand new paddle. "We want to present this to you," she said. "This paddle is used by Chinese players in international tournaments." On the box containing the gift were written the words "To a Japanese friend: Hurrah for China–Japan friendship!"

"Thank you. I am deeply grateful," Shin'ichi replied. "I hope you will definitely visit Japan in the future."

Shin'ichi also planted the seeds of friendship in the hearts of the younger generation. Thinking of the future, he engaged earnestly in dialogue. Dialogue is the starting point of all things.

IN AN ART CLASS, various works by the students were on display. Deeply impressed by the students' craftsmanship, Shin'ichi said: "You are very talented! These works are quite remarkable. I'd like to show these to children in Japan."

When Shin'ichi's words had been translated, the teacher and students quickly responded: "Please, feel free to take them with you. It will be a gift from us to our friends in Japan." And they gave Shin'ichi numerous drawings and other works to take home with him.

"Thank you. These are great treasures of friendship," Shin'ichi said.

A student then remarked with innocent enthusiasm, "I'm sure Japanese students will like China when they see these drawings."

In return, Shin'ichi presented the school with a tape recorder to help students in their language studies.

Leaving the classroom, Shin'ichi and his party went into the school courtyard where they noticed a group of students constructing something in a deep trench that they had dug themselves. The school representative guiding them said: "This trench is where we will take refuge if we are attacked by the Soviet Union. We are also building underground classrooms so we can continue studying in such a situation."

Shin'ichi was taken aback by these words, and he looked at Mineko. The looming shadows of war were affecting the students' daily life at school. No doubt the fear of a possible attack hovered over them as they worked diligently in the trench. It was a touching yet painful sight to behold.

Shin'ichi felt a sharp pang in his heart. He remembered digging bomb shelters in various parts of his own neighborhood during World War II, to take refuge in during air attacks. For him, it was a memory of some thirty years ago, but for his neighbors in China, it was a present reality.

Shin'ichi watched the scene intently, as if to engrave the image in his mind. He strongly said to himself: *I will tell the Soviet leaders about this, and urge them to pursue a course of peace. I will do everything I can, even at the risk of my own life, to prevent hostilities between China and the Soviet Union.* This was the greatest challenge facing Shin'ichi, but he was determined to succeed, no matter how impossible it seemed.

As Albert Einstein (1879–1955) once said, "Maybe, by raising my voice, I can help the greatest of all causes—good will among men and peace on earth."[16]

THE DENSE GREEN trees lining the shore of Kunming Lake sparkled in the sunlight. Fluffy white clouds floated in the blue sky above. On the morning of June 4, Shin'ichi and his party were invited to visit the Summer Palace on the outskirts of Beijing, a spacious garden that had been used by the Empress Dowager Cixi of the Qing dynasty as a detached palace. Atop the gentle rise of Longevity Hill stood a beautiful pavilion enclosed by the Long Corridor. The waters of Kunming Lake spread out before the building.

A dignified gentleman with white hair and a cane in hand stood at the entrance to the Summer Palace, awaiting Shin'ichi's arrival. It was China-Japan Friendship Association Vice President Zhao Puchu, who was also vice president and acting head of the Buddhist Association of China. Shin'ichi had met Mr. Zhao on his arrival in Beijing as well as at the welcome dinner put on by their Chinese hosts, but he hadn't had an opportunity to speak with him at length.

With a smile, Vice President Zhao said warmly: "I have

heard much about you, President Yamamoto. I was looking forward to meeting you in person." Mr. Zhao guided Shin'ichi and the others down the Long Corridor. They then went out on Lake Kunming on a sightseeing boat. Shin'ichi and Mr. Zhao enjoyed a lively conversation on Buddhism that continued over a meal at a restaurant situated at the foot of Longevity Hill. Mr. Zhao's teacher was a priest of the T'ien-t'ai school of Buddhism.

The vice president eventually began to talk about his struggles helping people during the Sino-Japanese War. He said: "There were so many people lying dead by the side of the road, having died from hunger, cold and illness. Most of them were infants and farmers. They were all so poor. But even though I witnessed such things, there was nothing we could do under the old social system that existed at that time."

Chinese Buddhism in those days was corrupt and degenerate, and actually contributed to the sufferings of ordinary people.

Mr. Zhao added with emphasis: "The original spirit of Buddhism is to serve the people. The people were suffering. But the Buddhists here did nothing. That was completely unacceptable!"

Shin'ichi's eyes flashed and he replied without hesitation: "You're absolutely right. Working selflessly for the sake of the people and society is the spirit of bodhisattvas, of the Buddha; it is the heart of Buddhist practitioners. There is no Buddhism without action." His voice was firm and confident.

SHAKYAMUNI STOOD up to liberate all living beings from the four sufferings of birth, aging, sickness and death. Buddhism teaches the fundamental way for people to free themselves from suffering. Borrowing the words of Vice President Zhao, the essence of Buddhist practice is the spirit of "serving the people."

Nichiren Daishonin, wishing to free people from suffering and enable them to attain happiness, engaged in a struggle to establish the correct teaching for the peace of the land, fully aware of the great persecution he would face in the attempt. His goal was to realize a peaceful society based on the Buddhist principle of compassion and respect for the sanctity of life. The mission of practitioners of Nichiren Buddhism begins with kosen-rufu, which represents a revolutionary religious movement, and ends with the realization of a peaceful society based on humanistic principles.

On a slightly different note, Mahatma Gandhi said that politics, too, should follow the path of truth taught by religion and that religion that abhors politics is not deserving of the name.[17]

Mr. Zhao and Shin'ichi were in complete agreement about the essence of Buddhism and recognized each other as kindred spirits. Shin'ichi recounted how the Soka Gakkai had fought against persecution from Japan's militarist government and asserted that the true role of religion was to serve society and the people. Vice President Zhao mentioned that he read a chapter of the Lotus Sutra each day, and from there, the conversation turned to the Lotus Sutra and T'ien-t'ai's three major works.[18]

Their dialogue was lively, and the two men often finished each other's sentences. For example, when Shin'ichi said, "Body and mind," Vice President Zhao responded with, "are inseparable." Mr. Zhao mentioned the "Practices and Vows of the Bodhisattva Universal Worthy" chapter of the Flower Garland Sutra. To which Shin'ichi replied: "'Universal' refers to human society. And 'worthy' can be interpreted as an individual upholding a faith-based philosophy. 'Practice' of course refers to action, and 'vow' is the wish to bring happiness to all people."

"That's a wonderful interpretation," Mr. Zhao said. He nodded in agreement as Shin'ichi spoke of a humanistic Buddhism grounded in reality. When the two men parted, Mr. Zhao commented: "I am deeply appreciative not only for your knowledge of Buddhism but your efforts for China–Japan friendship."

Shin'ichi replied: "I am also very grateful for your hospitality. Let's meet again and continue our discussion on Buddhism."

Shin'ichi and Vice President Zhao did meet on several future occasions, developing a warm and close friendship.

THE AMERICAN philosopher and educator John Dewey (1859–1952), speaking at Peking University, said, "Social progress is dependent upon educational progress."[19] Education is the key to a society's growth and development. As such, the future of a society, of a nation, can be determined by the quality of its universities.

After their visit to the Summer Palace, Shin'ichi and his party headed to Peking University. They were looking forward to meeting with the youth who would shoulder China's future. Peking University was one of the country's oldest universities. After the establishment of the

People's Republic of China, having absorbed the non-technical departments of Tsinghua University, it merged with and moved to the campus of what was formerly known as Yenching University.

Peking University was located about two miles from the Summer Palace. Passing through a traditional red gate, they entered the spacious, green campus. Shin'ichi and the others were given a warm welcome by the university's vice president, faculty members and student representatives. They were then escorted to the Lin Hu Xuan Reception Hall, where a discussion ensued. The building had been the residence of the Yenching University president.

Shin'ichi stated that he wished to donate five thousand books, including many in Japanese, to the university library in order to promote cultural exchange and mutual understanding between Japan and China, and he presented a list of the books to the vice president. He did this out of his hope that the youth of China would be able to study and learn more about Japan. Shin'ichi also presented the vice president with a commemorative medal from Soka University as well as a collection of essays by Soka University students about Chinese film. As Soka University's founder, Shin'ichi hoped that Soka University and Peking University would serve as bridges for future friendly relations between their two countries.

The vice president gave Shin'ichi a copy of the Peking University student newspaper, a photo collection on Chinese arts and crafts, and other gifts. Shin'ichi asked if the faculty members would sign the photo book and perhaps write a motto or inscription in it. He was always thinking about how to make each occasion deeply significant and how to forge strong heart-to-heart bonds with others. Sometimes the words inscribed in a book or on a decorative placard can become an important treasure for future generations. Shin'ichi always took action with the far distant future in mind.

In response to Shin'ichi's request, ten faculty members and student representatives signed the book and inscribed it with messages such as "Toward the eternal friendship of the people of China and Japan!"

AFTER OUTLINING the history and educational aims of Peking University for Shin'ichi and his party, the Peking University representatives gave them a tour of some of the university's facilities, including the gymnasium and the library. At that time, the university had twenty academic departments and seven non-degree graduate programs, and also operated seven factories. The factories had been built under the slogan of self-reliance for university students, faculty members and workers.

The biochemistry and pharmaceutical factory produced pharmaceuticals for the general populace. The students not only studied but had a social responsibility at the same time. The idea behind the program was to link study and work, thus enabling the participants to make a productive contribution to Chinese society. Another reason for having the students work in factories on campus was to prevent them from becoming alienated from the working people and from developing into some kind of "intellectual aristocracy." Shin'ichi felt as if he had glimpsed the fundamental spirit of China's educational revolution.

University education is certain to be different depending on the country and the age. Peking University's use of factories may have been a transitional method. The important thing to remember, however, is that the university's essential purpose is to protect, serve and contribute to the welfare of the entire population. There is no greater perversion than for leaders and members of the educated elite to lose sight of the importance of being directly connected to and serving the people and instead try to dominate the people for their own purposes.

Shin'ichi also spent time talking with the students studying Japanese at Peking University. Their fluency was extremely impressive. When he asked how long they had been studying the language, they replied just two

or three years. He asked a female student why she had decided to study Japanese. She replied enthusiastically, "I want to contribute to friendly bilateral relations and the mutual prosperity of our countries." No doubt she was studying hard each day, propelled by her high ideals and passionate conviction. Shin'ichi sensed the refreshing spirit of youth in her reply.

Shin'ichi and his traveling companions also joined in a friendly game of table tennis with the language students. Playing with these young people who spoke such fluent Japanese, Shin'ichi felt right at home, as if he were playing table tennis with Soka University students back in Japan.

AFTER TOURING the Peking University campus, Shin'ichi and his party returned to the Lin Hu Xuan Reception Hall and continued their discussion with the university vice president and faculty members. The world's focus was on Peking University as an institution contributing to the future of the new China. Shin'ichi asked several candid questions, such as the faculty's opinions on nuclear research, the admittance of foreign students to Peking University, the Chinese school entrance examination system and the importance of international exchange between university students and faculty.

Speaking from his heart, Shin'ichi said: "I would like to work with you to build a new age. I hope we can combine our efforts to surmount any obstacles that lie ahead on the way. That is my sincere wish, and for that reason, I hope we can engage in a frank discussion of opinions."

The university representatives responded to Shin'ichi's request by speaking seriously and honestly. It was a satisfying exchange of ideas, brimming with a shared passionate commitment to realizing a bright future. Passion inspires passion, and sincerity summons forth sincerity. Genuine dialogue is just this sort of profound life-to-life interaction.

It would be fair to say that this day marked the substantive beginning of a close relationship between Soka University and Peking University. Later, the two institutions signed an academic exchange agreement, in 1979, and set in motion a flow of students and faculty between them. Shin'ichi, the founder of Soka University, has personally built this golden bridge of educational exchange.

The future rests with young people. Opening the way forward for them is the key to a positive, hope-filled tomorrow.

Shin'ichi went on to deliver lectures at Peking University on three occasions (in 1980, 1984 and 1990), and Peking University was the first Chinese university to confer an honorary professorship upon him in 1984.

On the morning of the next day, June 5, Shin'ichi and the others headed northwest of Beijing by car. The trees lining the road were a beautiful green. Eventually, they began to pass through farmland with mountain ranges rising in the distance. They could see a stone and brick wall snaking along the mountains—the Great Wall of China. It was almost noon when they arrived at Badaling, the highest peak of the Jundu Mountain range, along which the wall ran. Escorted by China-Japan Friendship Association council member Jin Sucheng and others from the organization, Shin'ichi and his party walked along a section of the wall.

THE WALKWAY atop the Great Wall was approximately fifteen feet wide. Some sections of the wall rose at a very steep incline. Noticing Shin'ichi struggle to navigate these steep patches, a youth member of the China-Japan Friendship Association helped by supporting him from behind. "Thank you," Shin'ichi said, "but I want to be 'self-reliant.'" "Self-reliance" was China's national policy. Jin Sucheng laughed heartily at Shin'ichi's remark.

After they had climbed for some time, the view opened up before them and they could see the Yongding River sparkling in the distance. Beneath the bright, clear sky, the Great Wall looked like a giant dragon twisting through the green landscape.

Shin'ichi chatted pleasantly with Mr. Jin: "I've dreamed about standing here since I was a little boy. This is a historic day for me. My mentor, Josei Toda, often said that he would like us to visit China and stroll along the Great Wall together. I feel as if he is here with me today.

"Mr. Toda also said that we must build a citadel of capable individuals who would work for the happiness of the people. Countries and organizations ultimately come down to the people who comprise them. Everything depends upon how many committed, bright, courageous and sincere people can be fostered and united into a common force for good. That's why I am pouring my energies into education, for the sake of the twenty-first century."

The Indian poet Rabindranath Tagore (1861–1941) said: "A country is the creation of man. A country is not all land but all soul. It is only when its people are expressive

that a country is fully expressed."[20] Soka Gakkai activities enable people to shine, to express themselves fully.

Nodding, Mr. Jin remarked: "I agree completely. Everything comes down to the ability of people. And for people to fully demonstrate their abilities takes courage. A motto of the Chinese is: 'Those who do not wish to be enslaved must rise up. The people must become a Great Wall of thought and philosophy.' I believe that a spiritual Great Wall comprised of people who stand up courageously with a sound philosophy is the strongest thing of all. Nothing is a match for the Great Wall of the human spirit."

SHIN'ICHI SAID enthusiastically: "Yes, Mr. Jin, it's just as you say! The human spirit is the strongest force there is. It is the source of boundless wisdom and creative innovation. As long as our spirit remains unbroken, we will never be defeated, no matter how dire the situation. In life and in the struggle to change society, spiritual defeat always precedes actual defeat.

"Laziness, cowardice, carelessness, impatience, resignation, despair—all of these can corrode the spirit and lead to defeat. That's why we must forge and strengthen our inner fortitude. That's the purpose of philosophy.

"The Soka Gakkai has faced numerous storms of difficulties and hardships, but it has surmounted all, like the immortal phoenix. That's because regardless of the trials we've encountered, our hearts never retreated a single step."

Mr. Jin responded vigorously: "Yes, you have courageously called for the normalization of relations between our nations, and urged the signing of a bilateral peace and friendship treaty. Though harshly criticized, you remained undaunted. In your actions, I sense the strong and unshakable spirit that permeates the Soka Gakkai."

"Thank you," Shin'ichi replied. "Working for world peace is my personal mission. Building friendship between Japan and China is indispensable for the realization of that aim. That's why it must be achieved. I've acted based on that belief. Let's work together to construct a Great Wall of peace, a Great Wall of friendship and a Great Wall of the human spirit."

Shin'ichi said with a smile: "I am deeply grateful that we were able to have this life-to-life exchange transcending national differences, here on this wall that was built to keep out invaders from the north!"

Their conversation flowed on effortlessly. Their joyous

laughter rose into the blue sky. A beautiful drama of friendship was unfolding on the Great Wall of China, one of humanity's important cultural treasures.

That day, Shin'ichi and his party also visited the Dingling Museum. The museum is located at the site of the Dingling Tomb, one of the thirteen tombs of the Ming dynasty emperors. The group then viewed the nearby Ming Tombs Dam.

When Shin'ichi returned to his lodgings, a message was awaiting him—a meeting had been scheduled the following day with Vice Premier Li Xiannian.

O N THE MORNING of June 6, Shin'ichi and his party visited the Dashilan area of Beijing, a bustling shopping district south of Tiananmen Square. They went to see some bomb shelters that had been dug there beneath a department store. Someone opened a hatch on the store's ground floor, revealing a stairway leading below. When the group reached the bottom of the stairs, they discovered what might best be described as an underground city. It was well lit and clean, and was equipped with canteens, conference rooms, telephone rooms, control rooms and broadcasting centers. They were told that every district of the city was connected to all the others by underground passageways.

The Dashilan area was known for its department stores and movie theaters; on most days there were some eighty thousand people in the area and as many as two hundred thousand on holidays. Arrangements had been made so that, in an emergency, those people could reach the underground shelters within five or six minutes.

The person guiding Shin'ichi and the others explained, "It's been estimated that a missile from another country could reach here in seven minutes, so this gives our people plenty of time to get to safety."

The group was also shown the underground shelters constructed for nearby residential areas. They were told that most of the excavating had been done by women and the elderly, their average age being more than fifty.

Shin'ichi said to the guide: "Yesterday, we visited the Great Wall. This shelter is a subterranean Great Wall, isn't it?" The guide nodded. "Yes, that's right. We've built this to protect ourselves from an enemy attack. It is solely for self-defense. We have no intention of attacking any other nation. We won't be digging these tunnels all the way to Moscow." The guide smiled and added on a more solemn note: "First, we are opposed to war. But second, we are not afraid of it."

Shin'ichi said: "I see. I'll never forget your unity of purpose, passionate desire for peace and courageous spirit."

When Shin'ichi thought of the feelings of the Chinese people—their fear of an attack from the Soviet Union and their efforts to lift their spirits amid such anxiety—it pained him deeply.

"I will tell the world about what I've learned here," he remarked with firm resolve. Silently, he pledged to do everything in his power to bridge the gap of mistrust between China and the Soviet Union.

ON JUNE 6, Shin'ichi hosted a thank-you dinner for the Chinese friends he had made in Beijing. The event started at six in the evening at the Beijing

International Club. Invited were members of the China-Japan Friendship Association, including President Liao Chengzhi and his wife Jing Puchun, and Vice President Zhang Xiangshan, along with representatives from the places he had visited, such as the elementary school and the junior high school, Peking University, the factory and the people's commune, as well as staff members from the Beijing Hotel where he and his party were staying.

In his opening remarks, Shin'ichi expressed his profound gratitude, saying, "I will never forget the sincere goodwill exhibited by all my Chinese friends during our stay in Beijing." He then pledged: "I have stressed to the youth traveling with me the importance of forging genuine friendship with the people of China for generations to come. These are not just empty words to me. Please watch our future actions!" Shin'ichi was resolved to translate his sentiments into actions.

The American philosopher Ralph Waldo Emerson (1803–82) wrote, "Without [action], thought can never ripen into truth."[21]

A determination is only meaningful if it is put into action and produces results. Determination without action is nothing but wishful thinking.

President Liao Chengzhi responded to Shin'ichi's remarks, saying: "President Yamamoto has made tireless efforts for China–Japan friendship and the improvement of bilateral relations for many years now. He has stated on numerous occasions that the Soka Gakkai's resolve to maintain China–Japan friendship will never change, no matter what happens. And he has affirmed that he will wholeheartedly preserve and solidify the golden bridge of friendship linking our nations that has been built by those who have gone before us. I would like to take this opportunity to express my most profound praise and admiration for the deep personal commitment President Yamamoto and our friends of the Soka Gakkai have made to furthering friendship between our countries."

The dinner began over convivial conversation. Shin'ichi and Mineko went around to the five tables at which everyone was seated, sincerely thanking each person and promising to meet again. "I will visit Beijing many more times and bring many young people with me," Shin'ichi said. "Let's build a solid bridge of friendship." He exchanged firm handshakes with his guests in a pledge of lasting friendship.

AFTER THE DINNER, Shin'ichi and his traveling companions went with President Liao Chengzhi, Vice President Zhang Xiangshan and others from the China-Japan Friendship Association to the Great Hall of the People for their meeting with Vice Premier Li Xiannian. Arriving at the Great Hall just after nine that evening, Shin'ichi and the others were greeted warmly by the vice premier and his party, who were lined up at the entrance to the room where the meeting was to take place.

Vice Premier Li had participated in the harrowing Long March and, though gentle in demeanor, he exuded an air of fortitude and austerity, his eyes glinting with keen intelligence.

Shin'ichi shook hands firmly with each of the hosts. A landscape painting of Yan'an, the end point of the Long March, located in Shaanxi Province, hung in the meeting room, a spacious chamber with high ceilings. After everyone had been seated and introduced, Vice Premier Li said in a warm and friendly manner, "Please ask whatever you'd like."

Shin'ichi replied: "Thank you. Most of the members of our delegation this time are representatives of our youth division, their average age being thirty-five."

With a big smile, Vice Premier Li responded: "That's wonderful. Allow me to once again welcome you all to China."

The Chinese leader then traced the process Shin'ichi and his colleagues had gone through in promoting the restoration of diplomatic relations between China and Japan, remarking: "Your role has been extremely significant, President Yamamoto. You have made a tremendous contribution."

"Thank you for your kind words," Shin'ichi replied. "I have done everything I possibly could for the sake of Japan–China friendship and world peace."

To leave behind a brilliant record of achievement requires striving with all one's might each day, each moment, toward a lofty goal.

Vice Premier Li added: "Premier Zhou Enlai has expressed a deep interest in you, President Yamamoto, and in the Soka Gakkai. By rights, it should be the premier who is meeting you today, but he's in the hospital right now. He asked me to relay the message to you that he wants very much to meet you, but that it is just not possible this time. He sends you his warmest regards."

Shin'ichi later learned that Premier Zhou had undergone an operation for cancer only five days earlier.

PREMIER ZHOU ENLAI had been in poor health for some time. He had also suffered tremendously because of the Cultural Revolution. The Cultural Revolution began under the leadership of Communist Party Chairman Mao Zedong in order to preserve the revolutionary spirit forever and keep the class struggle alive, but it eventually became a tool in a political power struggle between various factions. The so-called Gang of Four, a group of Communist Party leaders—headed by Chairman Mao's wife, Jiang Qing—who supported the Cultural Revolution, used whatever fault or error they could find to attack any person or group who opposed or refused to follow them. In this way, one by one, they eliminated their rivals.

Premier Zhou Enlai became a target as well, and on one occasion, he was surrounded by the Red Guards and held captive in his offices. It was also around this time that he was diagnosed with cancer—in May 1972, two years before Shin'ichi's visit. Premier Zhou nevertheless remained hard at work as one of China's top leaders while undergoing repeated periods of hospitalization. His illness worsened, however, and so he finally consented to undergoing surgery.

In spite of how ill he was, Premier Zhou took great interest in Shin'ichi's visit. Through his representatives, he inquired about the smallest details pertaining to the comfort of Shin'ichi and his party, such as their culinary tastes and whether they smoked or not. Learning of this, Shin'ichi responded that they were overjoyed by the premier's consideration, but that the gesture was more than enough, and they required no special treatment. Still,

Premier Zhou gave instructions that the curtains in each of the Japanese visitors' rooms at the Beijing Hotel be changed to heavier ones in order to block out the light so that they could sleep better at night.

Shin'ichi also realized that this meeting with Vice Premier Li Xiannian had been arranged by Premier Zhou. He couldn't help but feel that the hospitalized premier was saying, "Please speak to the vice premier as if he were me."

The Scottish historian Thomas Carlyle (1795–1881) remarked, "Sincerity, a deep, great, genuine sincerity, is the first characteristic of all men in any way heroic."[22] How true this is.

Shin'ichi's discussion with Vice Premier Li was a friendly, earnest and richly productive exchange that focused on the future of Japan–China relations. Shin'ichi began by asking the vice premier's thoughts on a Japan–China peace and friendship treaty and went on to ask probing questions about ten topics in all, including socialism and individual freedom, China's natural resources, bureaucracy within organizations and nuclear weapons. Vice Premier Li responded readily to every question.

AWARE OF China's adversarial posture toward the two superpowers, the United States and the Soviet Union, Shin'ichi asked Vice Premier Li the following question: "What is the basic position of China with regard to the developed nations other than the United States and the Soviet Union, for example, Japan and the nations of Europe, as far as engagement and exchange are concerned?"

Vice Premier Li responded: "We are steadfastly committed to the Five Principles of Peaceful Coexistence,[23] one of which is noninterference in the internal affairs of other nations. Our relations with the nations you mentioned are developing in a positive direction. We may have differing opinions on some issues, but I think that's to be expected. After all, our social and political systems are different.

"Even as socialism advances in China, we have no intention of forcing our political or social system on others. It is up to the people of each nation to decide upon their own social system."

Shin'ichi believed the vice premier's words. They carried the weight of truth.

Count Richard Coudenhove-Kalergi (1894–1972), the Austrian thinker and proponent of European unification, observed, "Truth unites and connects; it destroys the barriers that fallacies and lies have erected between human beings."[24]

Shin'ichi continued: "In 1969, I called for Japan to give top priority to concluding a peace and friendship treaty with China. Such a treaty would be an important key to peace, not only for our two nations but for the rest of Asia and the world. I'd like to ask your opinion on this matter, as a representative of China, if I may."

It was a very direct question and the vice premier replied sincerely: "Relations between China and Japan are developing in a healthy direction. We would like to see a peace and friendship treaty concluded at the earliest possible date. But there are still some unresolved matters between our two governments that must be settled. And, more than anything, concluding a bilateral peace and friendship treaty needs to take place against the backdrop of growing friendship between our peoples at a grassroots level."

Shin'ichi and Vice Premier Li discussed many subjects of great importance not only for Japan but the entire world.

SHIN'ICHI THEN asked Vice Premier Li: "Any organization, when it grows to be very large, tends to become bureaucratic. How can that be prevented from happening?"

The vice premier replied: "The top leaders must be willing to hear the criticism of the people as well as be able to reflect on and critique themselves. They need to constantly bear in mind that if they begin to act like bureaucrats, they will be denounced by the people. And, remembering that the people are the arbiters of justice, they must constantly keep themselves in check. Bureaucracy can also be surmounted by leaders dedicating themselves to serving the people rather than sitting back and enjoying the fruits of their established organization."

Shin'ichi agreed completely with these insights. When leaders lose their commitment to serving the people, they start thinking only about protecting themselves; the organization they belong to grows rigid; and maintaining it becomes their main objective. People then become a means to an end and are regarded as existing for the sake of the organization rather than the other way around. In order for an organization to remain warm and humanistic, and continue functioning for the people's welfare, its leaders must never forget the spirit of serving the people.

In terms of the Soka Gakkai, this means serving the members. The future of the Soka Gakkai depends on whether its top leaders and Headquarters staff can preserve their dedication to serving the members. Leaders need to uphold and put into practice the principle that they are here to work for the happiness of the members. Such devotion and sincerity will win the members' trust and inspire unity.

Another important point for avoiding becoming bureaucratic is for leaders, whether of an organization or country, to exchange frank opinions and engage in open conversation and dialogue with the people they are meant to serve.

The Soka Gakkai has always advanced with dialogue as

its mainstay. Wherever Shin'ichi traveled, he spent a great amount of time talking candidly with local members. During large meetings, he also made an effort to prevent communication from becoming one-sided, fielding questions from the audience and addressing some members individually. The Soka Gakkai's humanism is found in such life-to-life exchange.

SHIN'ICHI ALSO wished to ask Vice Premier Li about the issue of succession in the Chinese leadership. This was a question that the Beijing correspondents of the major Japanese newspapers had also wanted Shin'ichi to pose. Shin'ichi broached the subject in a clever and playful manner: "Your name, Xiannian, literally means 'to think ahead' or to have foresight, doesn't it?" The vice premier laughed heartily.

"Since you have clear foresight, I'd like to ask you a frank question, if I may. The world is very interested to know who will eventually succeed Chairman Mao Zedong. Do you have any thoughts on the matter?"

The vice premier's expression immediately became guarded. Choosing his words carefully, he replied, "Chairman Mao is in very good health."

"I realize that is the case now, but I'm wondering about fifty or one hundred years from now," Shin'ichi pressed.

"Chairman Mao is in very good health," repeated the vice premier.

Sensing that he had brought up a touchy subject, Shin'ichi quickly changed the topic.

At the time, the Gang of Four was employing a wide variety of tactics to seize power after Chairman Mao was no longer on the scene. If the vice premier had said any-thing that could be deemed inappropriate, it would have been reported to the secret police and used as an excuse to bring about his downfall. What was actually taking place during the Cultural Revolution was mostly hidden from view, but both Vice Premier Li and Premier Zhou Enlai had been the targets of criticism. They knew that even the slightest error in judgment could put them at the mercy of their enemies, and each day was rife with tension.

Amid this climate, Premier Zhou and others like him continued to earnestly fulfill their duties while remaining constantly on the alert. They rode out the tempest rag-ing around them by calmly and tenaciously observing the changing currents of the times.

In January 1976, when Premier Zhou died, the Chi-nese people grieved deeply. They spoke out in protest against the powerful Gang of Four. It is the people who make history happen. Zhou Enlai observed, "No power can prevent the just actions of the people from advancing to victory."[25]

Vice Premier Li was one of those who stood up to drive out the Gang of Four. Eventually, he would serve as president of the People's Republic of China.

THE SUBJECT of nuclear arms also came up dur-ing Shin'ichi's meeting with Vice Premier Li, who stated unequivocally that China would never, under any circumstances, launch a first nuclear strike. The vice pre-mier further emphasized that his country had no inten-tion of pursuing a path of hegemony. Their discussion lasted for more than two hours and, in spite of being their first meeting, was a friendly, heart-to-heart exchange. Shin'ichi left feeling confident that China strongly desired peace.

After his late-night meeting with the vice premier, Shin'ichi met with members of the Japanese press corps and responded to their questions about his encounter with the Chinese leader. The front page of the evening edition of the *Asahi Shimbun* newspaper the following day, June 7, carried the headline, "Communist China Intent on Peace with Japan and Europe Even As Socialism Progresses, Says Vice Premier Li Xiannian." Shin'ichi's talk with the vice premier was covered in detail in the article that followed.

It was nearly midnight when Shin'ichi arrived back at his lodgings. The next day, he was scheduled to travel to Xi'an, departing at seven in the morning. While packing, he said to Mineko: "Today, June 6, is Mr. Makiguchi's birthday. Mr. Makiguchi thought very highly of the Chinese students who were studying in Japan during his day, and he had great respect for them."

In his midthirties, Tsunesaburo Makiguchi was a teacher of geography at Kobun College in Tokyo, a school for students from China. The Chinese writer Lu Xun studied there at the time. Chinese students who were inspired by Mr. Makiguchi's work *The Geography of Human Life* later translated it into Chinese and published it.

Shin'ichi added: "On Mr. Makiguchi's birthday, I had a meaningful discussion with Vice Premier Li, in which we talked about opening a path of friendship between Japan and China. Mr. Toda also often spoke about the need to contribute to the happiness of the people of Asia.

He was deeply familiar with Chinese history and literature, including the Chinese classic *The Compendium of Eighteen Histories*, and had a strong love for China. I'm sure that Mr. Makiguchi and Mr. Toda are very happy about this meeting."

Mineko smiled and nodded, remarking, "I can just imagine how happy they must be."

Both Shin'ichi and Mineko were tired, but thinking of their mentors filled them with energy. For a true disciple, a mentor is a source of courage and vitality.

O N JUNE 7, Shin'ichi and his party departed from Beijing Airport for Xi'an shortly after eight in the morning. The flight lasted about ninety minutes. China-Japan Friendship Association Secretary-General Sun Pinghua accompanied them as their guide. Xi'an is the capital of Shaanxi Province. Known as Chang'an in former times, it was the capital of China for many years. The city played an important role as a crossroads of Eastern and Western civilizations and was visited by Japanese envoys to China in the Tang dynasty. It was also the scene of the Xi'an Incident in 1936, which was a major turning point in modern Chinese history.

In December 1936, the Kuo-mintang's Northeast Army led by Zhang Xueliang, and its Northwest Army led by Yang Hucheng were both stationed at Xi'an, where they were preparing to launch a strike against the Chinese communist forces. But the two armies were convinced by the plea of the Communist Party that now was the time for all Chinese factions to put aside their differences and unite in the fight against the invading Japanese military forces. When the Kuo-mintang leader Generalissimo Chiang Kai-shek arrived from Nanjing (Nanking) to encourage his troops, they detained him and tried to persuade him to cease fighting the communists and instead join them in the struggle against the Japanese. This was the Xi'an Incident.

Zhou Enlai of the Communist Party led the negotiations, and eventually Chiang Kai-shek agreed to the Communist proposal. In July 1937, the Marco Polo Bridge Incident[26] occurred, marking the beginning of the Sino-Japanese War (1937–45). In China, the Xi'an Incident led to the Second Kuomintang-CCP (Chinese Communist Party) United Front, as a result of which an Anti-Japanese National United Front was created.

After arriving in Xi'an, Shin'ichi and his party were given a tour of a textile factory. Many Chinese women were working happily away at the plant, which had a kindergarten and other facilities that enabled women with families to work without anxiety. When women are treated with consideration and respect, they are able to take action freely and energetically, which gives rise to fresh development. Shin'ichi sensed China's bright future in the cheerfully working women.

The Swedish thinker and educator Ellen Key (1849–1926) wrote, "No profound spiritual transformation has ever taken place unless women have taken part in it."[27]

SHIN'ICHI AND HIS party visited the home of one of the factory workers and had an opportunity to talk with her family members. Afterward, they visited the Memorial Museum of the Eighth Route Army Xi'an

Office, the former head office of the Chinese Communist Party.

Located on the grounds of Xi'an Castle, the office was set up after the Xi'an Incident as the Red Army Liaison Office. The struggle between the Kuomintang and the CCP continued even after the establishment of the united front. Yan'an, the stronghold of the revolution, was some 186 miles away from Xi'an. The Xi'an office played an important role as a center for communications with Yan'an as well as an outpost and frontline base for advancing the communist cause. Young people who wished to enlist in the CCP forces would be interviewed and examined here, then sent on to Yan'an, where they would be educated and trained as fighters for the revolutionary struggle.

Shin'ichi and the others toured the interior of the memorial museum. A staff member showed them around the facility, including the underground level, where a security office was located. It was a very small room. A hole in the floor of the room housed the hand-operated motor that had been used to power the secret communications receiver. Kuomintang forces had destroyed their transmitter, and this receiver had been the only link the CCP members in Xi'an had with their headquarters. The reason it was hand-operated was that they couldn't risk tapping into the regular power supply above ground for fear of discovery.

In order to ensure that the receiver remained undetected, they would limit its use from midnight to four in the morning. After that, they disassembled it and stored the parts in different locations. As he listened to this explanation, Shin'ichi sensed the extreme caution of the CCP members in their determination to thoroughly and resolutely protect their means of communication. Indeed, extreme caution is crucial in any struggle. Carelessness can cause a fissure that can bring about the downfall of even the strongest fortress. A lack of caution can lead to ruin.

It is when we start to think that we've done enough that we become careless and negligent. This is exactly when the enemy strikes. It is not the enemy without that we should fear, but our inner enemies—our own spiritual weakness and laxity. Nichiren Daishonin writes, "Though the embankment between rice fields is firm, if there is an ant hole in it, then surely, in the long run, it will not remain full of water" (WND-I, 626).

SEVERAL KUOMINTANG observation posts had surrounded the Office of the Eighth Route Army, but the majority of the Xi'an population had supported the CCP office and had done what they could to protect it in every possible way. The guide said proudly, "The people would not have stood by silently if this office had been destroyed."

Nothing is stronger than the people's support. There is nothing to fear if we have wholeheartedly appealed to the people and won their agreement and support. The key to victory for any movement is to become more deeply aligned with the people, to find a place in the people's hearts.

One young man had been responsible for cranking the motor of the receiver. Believing in the future of his country, he turned the device with all his might. Now he was the head of the museum, and seemed to be already in his fifties. His parents both died of hunger before the People's Republic of China was established. That was why he had devoted his youth to the ideal of building a new China. He by no means forgot the pain and anger he felt because of his parents' deaths, which were due to the injustices of pre-revolutionary Chinese society. But it was for that reason that he was so grateful for China's liberation and why, with pride in his country, he firmly resolved to continue serving the people.

This history had also been communicated to the younger generation. The young woman guiding Shin'ichi and his party around the museum was herself very familiar with what had happened in the past and felt tremendous pride that her country had given freedom to so many formerly oppressed people. As long as the truths of history are firmly implanted in the hearts of young people, the revolutionary spirit will be preserved and passed on forever.

The museum head also spoke with great respect about Zhou Enlai, who had visited the office when he was still young to negotiate with top Kuomintang leaders in the final days of the Sino-Japanese War. "We had no cars then," he said. "The office staff prepared a rickshaw especially for him, but Premier Zhou refused to ride in it, saying that he preferred to walk. I was very impressed to see a high-ranking party official behave in such a modest and unassuming fashion."

No matter how fine our words, if they aren't matched by our actions, people won't trust us. Behavior and character are the greatest persuaders.

O N THE EVENING of June 7, Shin'ichi and his party were invited to a banquet, where they made new friends. On the morning of the following day, they visited the Shaanxi Provincial Museum (present-day Shaanxi History Museum), where they perused an exhibit depicting Shaanxi through the various dynasties that had risen and fallen there over the years—including the Zhou, Qin, Han, Sui and Tang. In the past, Xi'an (formerly Chang'an) had been a flourishing capital of the Silk Road, a trade route linking the civilizations of East and West.

Among the earliest artifacts of the Zhou dynasty on display was a drawing called "Slave with Horse Carrying Silk on Its Back" that seemed to be comparing the worth of different commodities. According to the accompanying explanation, its message was that a single horse and a single bolt of silk were worth five slaves—an indication of how lightly human life was regarded at the time. The picture conveyed the suffering of countless ordinary people that lay behind the luxurious lives of the ruling classes of the time. There was also a picture depicting farmers engaged in an uprising against the oppressive rulers of the Former and Later Han dynasties.

The museum was a virtual treasure trove of information communicating the significance of China's evolution from an age of dynastic rule, centered on the emperor, to the establishment of the People's Republic of China, in which the people were the protagonists of their society.

Another panel display recorded in detail the number of official envoys that had been sent from Japan to China—a total of 2,142. Of course, this did not include the numerous individuals who were lost at sea or killed on the treacherous voyage there. In other words, more than one thousand years ago, many Japanese had risked their lives to cross the ocean and engage in cultural exchange with neighboring China. But the bonds of friendship that both nations had long cultivated were later severed by human actions. Such divisiveness only reverses history's flow toward human harmony. What would the youthful envoys who had braved the difficult journey from Japan to China so many centuries ago have to say about such an unfortunate turn of events?

Today there are airplanes, and we can fly over miles of storm-tossed sea in just a few hours. But the doorway to exchange between Japan and China had only just been opened, and the psychological distance between both nations' people remained huge. Shin'ichi thought: *I will build an eternally indestructible bridge of Japan–China friendship. I will create an age in which an unending stream of young people can travel back and forth across that bridge and forge ties of deep friendship, like true brothers and sisters.*

Taking action with a clear vision for a new age gives rise to hope. A person with high ideals brims with courage and strength.

AFTER TOURING the Shaanxi Provincial Museum, Shin'ichi and his party went to visit the Da Ci'en Temple, about 0.62 miles south, which dated back to the seventh century. The temple's Dayan Pagoda had been built as a storehouse for the numerous manuscripts that the Chinese Buddhist monk Hsüan-tsang (Xuanzang) had brought back from India and translated into Chinese. Originally five stories high, the pagoda was later expanded to seven stories, rising to a height of two hundred ten feet.

One of the aims of the young Japanese monks traveling to China as official envoys was to study Buddhist texts in the capital of Chang'an (Xi'an). No doubt they spent a good deal of time poring over the texts stored in the Dayan Pagoda.

Hsüan-tsang entered the priesthood at an early age and went on to study various schools of Buddhist thought, but he was puzzled by what appeared to be discrepancies among the various teachers. Thus deciding to study Buddhism from the original texts, he traveled to India, the birthplace of Buddhism, crossing vast deserts and treacherous mountain paths to get there. He was a youth in his twenties at the time, and his powerful determination to study Buddhism is what motivated him to undertake the daunting journey. A seeking spirit gives rise to courage and strength, and it is advancing with a seeking spirit that enables us to grow as human beings.

Hsüan-tsang went to various sites throughout India, devoting himself to Buddhist practice and study and to researching Sanskrit texts. After more than a decade, he began the long trip back to Chang'an, carrying many Buddhist scriptures and statues with him. After returning home, he translated seventy-five Buddhist scriptures in 1,335 volumes into Chinese.

Shin'ichi said to his traveling companions: "Unfortunately, Hsüan-tsang didn't understand the essence of the Lotus Sutra. Nichiren Daishonin was very critical of his translations as well. Nevertheless, Hsüan-tsang had an enormous influence on the rise of Buddhist culture.

"It's very important to record teachings in writing in order to communicate them to future generations. That's why I am striving to document the true spirit of Nichiren's teachings. Every day is an intense struggle. I pour my life into speaking and writing each day, as if imparting my final wishes. And many Soka Gakkai members proficient in foreign languages are working day and night to translate those words. Their efforts may be inconspicuous, but they are playing a crucial role in spreading our kosen-rufu movement around the globe."

From there, he began to discuss worldwide kosen-rufu.

THAT AFTERNOON, Shin'ichi and his party visited Xi'an's Banpo Museum, which was built on the site of an excavated Neolithic village. They also visited the Mausoleum of the First Qin Emperor and the beautiful Huaqing Pool. In the evening, Shin'ichi hosted a thank-you dinner at the Xi'an People's Hotel for all those who had assisted and befriended them in Xi'an.

The following day, June 9, they traveled to Shanghai, departing on a 1:40 PM flight from Xi'an Airport. The plane was scheduled to stop in Zhengzhou, Henan Province, and in Nanjing, Jiangsu Province, on the way. They reached Zhengzhou at three in the afternoon. While they were waiting in the airport to reboard the plane and resume their flight, China-Japan Friendship Association Secretary-General Sun Pinghua, who was traveling with them, came up to Shin'ichi and said with a regretful expression: "Our connecting flight has been canceled because of a strong thunderstorm in the Nanjing area. I'm very sorry, but I'm afraid we'll have to stay overnight in Zhengzhou."

"I understand. Thank you for your help," Shin'ichi replied brightly. The rest of his party, however, looked worried.

Everything doesn't always go according to plan. Life is, in fact, a constant series of unexpected developments. The important thing is to not become fazed by such changes, but to use our wisdom to create the most positive outcome. Such flexibility and adaptability are signs of genuine strength as a human being.

Smiling, Shin'ichi said: "It's wonderful that we have an opportunity to stay here overnight, isn't it? I've always been fascinated by Zhengzhou."

Zhengzhou is the capital of Henan Province and a major distributor of wheat and cotton. It once flourished as the capital of the ancient Yin dynasty.

Shin'ichi's tone was upbeat as he continued: "The area of Henan Province, located in the middle reaches of the Yellow River, is in the center of China. It is also known as Zhongyuan, or the central plain. The Chinese people waged many battles to gain control of this region.

"A famous Chinese saying from this area speaks of 'hunting for deer in Zhongyuan' (*Zhong yuan zhu lu*), which basically means to fight for hegemony in China. '*Zhongyuan*' represents the heart of China, and 'deer' is a reference to the imperial throne."

Shin'ichi communicated his excitement at being in this richly historic place to the young people traveling with him.

SHIN'ICHI AND HIS party were able to secure lodgings at the Zhongzhou Hotel, and they went there to check in. In spite of the unexpected nature of their visit to Zhengzhou, representatives of the Henan Province Sub-Council of the Chinese People's Association for Friendship with Foreign Countries welcomed them warmly. They all enjoyed pleasant conversation as they dined together.

Shin'ichi said to the leader of the Henan Province Sub-Council officials: "Because of a sudden thunderstorm, we've been given this chance to stop over in Zhengzhou, a place in which I've always been very interested, and to make new friends in China. I wish to offer my heartfelt thanks to the thunderstorm." Everyone laughed.

The evening proved to be a wonderful opportunity to meet some of the residents of Zhengzhou. Shin'ichi was determined to forge strong ties of friendship that would last into the future. Doing so came down to his being open, sincere and passionate, and engaging those he met in heart-to-heart dialogue. The conversation flowed easily as they spoke of the history and culture of Henan Province. Because Cao Cao (Ts'ao Ts'ao) of the Kingdom of Wei had conquered the Zhongyuan area during the Three Kingdoms period in the third century, the conversation turned to the novel the *Romance of the Three Kingdoms*, a fictionalized account of that period.

Shin'ichi said: "My mentor, second Soka Gakkai president Josei Toda, had us young people read the *Romance of the Three Kingdoms* and other works, using them to instruct us in human nature and the art of leadership. My mentor especially loved the song 'A Star Falls in the Autumn Wind Over the Wuzhang Plains,' about the final years of Chuko K'ung-ming (Zhuge Liang), the prime minister of the Kingdom of Shu-Han [and one of the protagonists of the story]. The song was written by the great Japanese poet Bansui Doi. The young people here with me today would like to sing this song for you."

Everyone applauded, and the youth traveling with Shin'ichi stood up and began to sing. Their voices reverberated through the room.

Chuko K'ung-ming had defeated the Wei forces at the Battle of Red Cliffs and won many other very important victories, but in his battle against the same Wei forces at the Wuzhang Plains, he was struck down by illness. His condition was very grave, and it appeared that the Shu Han army he led would be defeated. The song described Chuko K'ung-ming's undying devotion as he contemplated the future of Shu Han and wondered who would save the suffering and oppressed people.

SHIN'ICHI HAD an unforgettable memory related to the song "A Star Falls in the Autumn Wind Over the Wuzhang Plains." On January 5, 1953, a dozen or so disciples gathered together with their mentor, Josei Toda, for a party commemorating the New Year held at a Chinese restaurant in Tokyo. One of the young men present sang this song for Mr. Toda on that occasion. Shin'ichi had suggested doing so at a meeting that took place at his home the day before. This was because he felt there was something in common between Chuko K'ung-ming, who had bravely taken the fate of the Shu Han Kingdom on his shoulders, and the spirit of Josei Toda, who had risen up resolutely to achieve kosen-rufu.

Listening intently to the young man's song, Mr. Toda's eyes filled with tears from time to time. Eventually, he removed his glasses and took out a handkerchief to dab his eyes. When the youth finished, Mr. Toda said: "That's a wonderful song. It's so moving. Would you please sing it again?"

Shin'ichi stood up with him to sing the song. Together, they sang passionately, their hearts filled with solemnity. Mr. Toda also sang softly along with them. He no longer even tried to wipe his tears away.

When the song came to an end, he asked them to sing it again, and this was repeated until they had sung it six times. Mr. Toda then said, "Do you really understand the spirit of this song?" He went on to explain that it conveyed Chuko K'ung-ming's deep anguish at knowing that death was near while he still had so much crucial work left to do. This was precisely Mr. Toda's own feeling.

"My body, too, is wracked by illness," he continued. "If I collapse, what will become of kosen-rufu? Aware of the great and important mission I shoulder, I simply cannot collapse. I cannot die, even if I wanted to!" It was an earnest cry that came from the depths of his being.

Speaking of the line in the song, "Ah, in the middle of the night on the Wuzhang Plains, the storm howls and the dew weeps," he said in a voice trembling with emotion: "Chuko K'ung-ming dies in the end. This line sings sadly of the failure of his mission. Of course, he went down in history as a great hero, but failure is failure, all the same.

"I cannot allow myself to fail. If the great work of kosen-rufu fails, the future of humanity will be dark indeed."

JOSEI TODA'S statement that he could not allow himself to fail struck Shin'ichi to the very core. Whether or not the great vow of the mentor is achieved comes down to the struggle of disciples. Shin'ichi was therefore determined to never accept defeat or failure in any struggle for kosen-rufu. He resolved to himself: I will become an invincible champion. Even the smallest defeat could hinder President Toda's vision of kosen-rufu. A true disciple continues to win no matter what!

From that moment on, Shin'ichi consistently raised the victory banner—in his struggles in Tokyo's Bunkyo Ward, in Sapporo, in Osaka, in Yamaguchi and wherever else he went. Victory is the hallmark of a true disciple.

Now in Zhengzhou, as he listened to the young people in his party passionately sing "A Star Falls in the Autumn Wind Over the Wuzhang Plains," Shin'ichi thought of his mentor and his lifelong cherished wish for the happiness of the people of China and the rest of Asia. At the same time, Shin'ichi made a profound pledge that, as Mr. Toda's disciple, he would devote his life to realizing his mentor's vision and create a golden bridge of friendship between Japan and China.

When the song was over, everyone applauded vigorously. One of the Chinese representatives smiled and remarked: "That's a wonderful song. I was deeply moved. I am truly happy that this song about Chuko K'ung-ming, who desired prosperity and peace for the people, has been performed here in Zhongyuan as a song of friendship."

The hour grew late as the group enjoyed a warm and unforgettable exchange.

At about that time, the Soka Gakkai Headquarters in

Tokyo was in a panic, wondering what had happened to Shin'ichi and his party. Kaoru Tahara and others traveling with Shin'ichi had tried several times to make an international telephone call from their lodgings to inform the Headquarters that they were staying overnight in Zhengzhou, but perhaps due to a shortage of phone lines, they were unable to get through. Meanwhile, the staff in Tokyo had contacted the lodgings where Shin'ichi and the others were expected to stay that night in Shanghai, only to be told that the Japanese party had not arrived.

The top Soka Gakkai leaders were deeply concerned and wondered what could have happened. They prayed earnestly for the group's safety. It wasn't until the next morning, when Shin'ichi and the others arrived at the hotel in Shanghai and were able to reach the headquarters in Tokyo, that the leaders there finally breathed a sigh of relief.

AT HALF PAST seven the next morning, June 10, Shin'ichi and his party checked out of their lodgings in Zhengzhou and boarded a plane for Shanghai, via Nanjing. Above Nanjing they had a view of China's longest river, the Yangtze. The river waters, sparkling in the sun, seemed to stretch on forever like a beautiful silver sash.

The group reached Shanghai at eleven that morning. A center of trade, manufacturing and commerce, the city was bustling. After eating lunch, they went to visit the Guangming Electric Plating Factory. The words, "A Warm Welcome to the Soka Gakkai Delegation Members from Japan!" along with colorful drawings of flower bouquets were written on a blackboard at the factory entrance.

The health of employees and preservation of the environment were top priorities at this factory, and various measures had been taken to safely dispose of the waste products of the electric plating process. The factory interior was also clean and neat. All wastewater was chemically purified, and the factory actually kept fish in it.

Speaking with the factory manager and others, Shin'ichi said: "I am very impressed by the conditions here. It's remarkable. In Japan, industrial development resulted in serious pollution. This was because profit was given priority over human life. Placing too much emphasis on the pursuit of wealth and convenience at the expense of human health and life is a terrible perversion of values. Treasuring and protecting life are universal, golden rules for the very survival of humankind. And Buddhism teaches those fundamental principles."

Shin'ichi didn't want the failures of Japan, which had been a kind of guinea pig for industrial pollution, to be repeated elsewhere. That's why he spoke with such urgency: "Pollution is a problem that people everywhere have to work on together to avoid. I hope you will communicate the importance your factory places on respecting and protecting life to others throughout China and the rest of Asia."

Environmental destruction tends to accompany the advance of modernization. That is why Shin'ichi was convinced that people must pool their wisdom across national boundaries and strengthen their cooperative efforts to protect the environment.

"AS LONG AS I remain alive, of course I must study."[28] Shin'ichi was riveted by these words. They had been written by the Chinese author Lu Xun in a letter two months before his death. After the electric plating factory, Shin'ichi and his party visited Lu Xun's former residence, which was situated on a stone-paved street. Lu Xun lived in Shanghai for nine years, and spent the last three-and-a-half years of his life in this three-story brick house. The living room on the ground floor had been preserved exactly as it was when Lu Xun was alive. There were five heavy wooden chairs set before a heavy, dark, wooden table. The words that so powerfully struck Shin'ichi were displayed on the wall of the room behind the living room. He looked silently at this line from Lu Xun's letter for some time.

This almost greedy desire to continue learning throughout life was without a doubt the fundamental spirit of Lu Xun, who continually opened new paths and was dedicated to changing his country. When we forget the desire to learn and improve ourselves, we become apathetic and complacent. With such an attitude, only defeat and decline will await us. It is by constantly challenging ourselves, by continuously moving forward, that we can experience life's dynamism and savor genuine victory.

Lu Xun died on October 19, 1936, at the age of fifty-five. The bed where he passed away still remained in the second-floor bedroom of the house. The calendar showed the day of his death, and the clock was stopped at the hour of his passing—5:25 AM.

Lu Xun had been one of Shin'ichi's favorite writers from his youth. In Lu Xun's works, Shin'ichi had sensed the author's powerful outrage at the contradictions and injustices of society and his heartfelt call for the people to become strong.

Lu Xun had become a writer in order to awaken and rally the people. He unsparingly depicted society's evils and injustices with eloquence and a discerning eye.

Lu Xun had been born into a wealthy family in Shaoxing, Zhejiang Province, in 1881, but the family fortunes declined when he was still a boy. In 1902, he traveled to Japan to study, hoping to become a physician.

AFTER STUDYING Japanese at Kobun College in Tokyo, Lu Xun enrolled in the Sendai Medical School (the forerunner of Tohoku University's School of Medicine). But in his second year, he suddenly abandoned his medical studies. In the preface to his novel *Call to Arms*, Lu Xun explains in detail what led to this decision. It seems that during a classroom slide presentation, he was struck by one particular image. It showed a Chinese man standing in the center, bound and tied. He had been apprehended as a spy for the Russians, and the Japanese imperial army was publicly beheading him to make an example of him. A crowd of robust-looking Chinese men were standing around watching him with apathetic expressions.

Describing his shock and outrage at this image, Lu Xun wrote, "The people of a weak and backward country, however strong and healthy they might be, could only serve to be made examples of or as witnesses of such futile spectacles."[29] He realized that the only way to truly help his people was to inspire them to "change their spirit."[30] Thus concluding that medical science was not so important after all, he quit his medical studies and resolved to dedicate his life to writing.

Nichiren Daishonin says, "It is the heart that is important" (WND-1, 1000). Our personal happiness and the well-being of society come down to what is in our hearts and minds. We need to train our hearts—our spirits—to be both strong and perceptive. We mustn't allow ourselves to be deluded by the illusory walls created by our inner cowardice or complacence. It is when people resolve to win and take action with courage and perseverance based on a strong spirit and vibrant life force that the dawn of a new age arrives.

Eventually, Lu Xun returned to China and, while working as an educator, took up his pen and began to write tirelessly with the aim of inspiring a change in people's hearts. He published the novels *The Diary of a Madman* and *The True Story of Ah Q,* as well as becoming a prolific essayist, critic and translator of foreign literature. He fought relentlessly against the feudalistic ideology and social order, and the government policies that had oppressed the Chinese people and rendered them powerless.

His heart beat with the revolutionary spirit and the dynamism of youth. Lu Xun also loved young people and gave his all to fostering them throughout his life. That is why, thinking of the young people who bought his books, he continued to pour his heart into producing works that would lead them in the right direction.

LU XUN WAS ALSO harshly criticized by some of the young people he educated and fostered, but in spite of that, he continued to believe in their potential. And whenever a young person was killed as a result of government oppression, he wept bitter tears and wrote in their memory. A photograph taken just eleven days before Lu Xun's death shows him talking with a group of youth.

The Chinese writer once said, "It is a joy to nurture others, even though one knows doing so means growing weaker and frailer, one drop of blood at a time."[31] These words perfectly captured Shin'ichi's feelings as well. He, too, had given his all to fostering youth. He was determined to be their steppingstone and springboard, and was willing to sacrifice himself for them. In fact, his reason for inviting youth representatives to join him on this first visit to China was based on his wish to serve as a guide or foundation for them so that they could build a golden bridge of peace and friendship between Japan and China.

Shin'ichi remarked to the person showing them around Lu Xun's former residence: "I am very grateful for the opportunity to see this important and significant historical treasure. I'm deeply moved. I will write of Lu Xun's life and work from time to time to make them more widely known in both Japan and the rest of the world."

Shin'ichi and his party next went to the nearby Hongkou Park, the location of Lu Xun's grave, set in an area shaded by trees. A statue of Lu Xun stood in front of the grave. It depicted the writer sitting with proud dignity in a chair. Looking up at the figure, Shin'ichi said: "He looks happy. It must be because he fought for his beliefs."

Those who have fought for their beliefs have no regrets. They burn with passion and genuine fulfillment. The ancient Roman emperor and philosopher Marcus Aurelius Antoninus said, "A man's true delight is to do the things he was made for."[32] True happiness belongs to those who struggle and strive for the sake of truth and justice and the welfare of others.

That night, another welcome banquet was held for Shin'ichi and his party in Shanghai. The youth traveling with Shin'ichi sang the Soka Gakkai favorite "Song of Comrades," contributing to a joyous and lively atmosphere.

SHANGHAI IS a very important industrial center of the People's Republic of China. New products of both light and heavy industry made there were on display in the Shanghai Exhibition Center, which Shin'ichi and the rest of his delegation visited on the morning of June 11. The center was like a large palace with a spire on top, and it was very spacious. More than five thousand industrial products were on display. Shin'ichi and his party were given a tour by the head of the center, who explained in detail the various items they came across—a steam turbine electrical generator, automobiles, boats, bicycles, electronic computers and other goods.

The center head's explanations overflowed with a sense of pride and passion, and it was clear from his attitude that China was deeply committed to developing its industrial sector. Perhaps many of the products were not quite as advanced as those of the West or Japan, but when Shin'ichi considered the productive and creative energy of the Chinese, he was certain that the day would come when China would lead the world.

"If Japan is overconfident of its technological capacities and doesn't keep on its toes, China may well surpass it in the twenty-first century," he remarked to his traveling companions. The key to future success is people's dedication and desire for progress. If we want to see what the future will bring, all we need to do is observe the spirit of the people—and of youth, in particular.

Shin'ichi and his party next visited the Shanghai Children's Palace, a center for after-school activities, located in the Luwan District. Shin'ichi said eagerly to his wife, Mineko: "We're going to have a chance to meet more children. It's an opportunity to talk with China's future!"

Having been on the road for thirteen days, Shin'ichi had reached the peak of exhaustion, but the thought of meeting more children renewed his energy. The purpose

of this trip was to build a bridge of friendship for the sake
of the future, and he was very excited about such opportunities. Shin'ichi was in complete earnest each moment.
He poured his entire being into every event and encounter. Doing so cleared his exhaustion and filled him with
fresh energy and determination.

BY THE TIME Shin'ichi and the others arrived at
the Shanghai Children's Palace in the Luwan District, the rain that had been falling that morning had
stopped. As they walked along the stone pavement freshly
washed by the rain, they heard applause. The official in
charge of the facility was there with teachers and students
to warmly greet the visitors. The children said cheerfully
in Chinese: "Welcome to our guests from Japan! Thank
you for coming." A girl in the upper grades of elementary
school, with dimples in her cheeks, and a girl in the lower
grades, wearing a charming hair ribbon, each stepped
forward to take one of Shin'ichi's hands and lead him
through the facility. As part of the welcome ceremony,
another girl explained the purpose and the history of the
children's center. Teachers also spoke.

There were children's centers like this in every district of Shanghai. They were places where local children
gathered to play games, participate in physical education
activities, take humanities and science courses, and learn
about contributing to the welfare of the community.
The faculty of the children's centers comprised not only
qualified teachers but also factory workers, technicians
and others.

Children need places other than school where they can

learn how to utilize their individuality and other unique qualities. In Japan, in particular, where a disproportionate emphasis is placed on the accumulation of knowledge, it could be said that there is a great need for education that teaches students about life and developing themselves as individuals. The activities conducted by the Soka Gakkai future division are a pioneering example of such extra-curricular education. Without a doubt, society's expectations of the Soka Gakkai will only grow in the future. Madame Soong Ching-ling (also Song Qingling), the wife of Sun Yat-sen and vice president of the People's Republic of China, declared, "Children are our future and hope."[33]

What can adults offer children? They can offer them peace. They can offer them a society that reveres life and respects human rights, a society with a bright future. Doing so is the responsibility of adults. Adults must fight for the sake of their children's future, and they must win in that struggle.

When the children and palace faculty finished their presentations, Shin'ichi said a few words: "I've come from Japan. I have looked forward to meeting you all. This is the highlight of my visit."

SMILING, SHIN'ICHI continued: "The members of the Soka Gakkai's Fuji Fife and Drum Corps have given me some gifts for you—a music record and twenty fifes. The record is of their heartfelt performance of the Chinese song 'Xiao pengyou' (Little Friends). They also made by hand the cloth cases the fifes are wrapped in." Shin'ichi additionally presented the students with a tape recorder and some other gifts to assist with their language-learning courses.

A little girl then stood up and said: "I have just composed a poem to express our feelings to you. Please listen to it." And she immediately began to recite the poem.

> *A present from our uncles*
> *and aunts.*
> *Our hearts ring with joy.*
> *Each gift is a sign*
> *of friendship.*
> *The hearts of the Chinese*
> *and Japanese people*
> *are brought together.*

Shin'ichi applauded enthusiastically. "That's wonderful!" he said. "Thank you. You're a great poet." Nothing delighted him more than to see children developing a poetic spirit.

Shin'ichi and the others next went around and observed the various classrooms in the facility. Entering a calligraphy class, they noticed a work by a seven-year-old boy displayed on the wall. The characters were beautifully written. It said: "My grandfather became a beggar when he was seven. Because of famine, my father had to leave his hometown and take up a life of wandering when he was seven. This year I'm seven, and I'm very happy to be able to attend school and study."

The Chinese people had experienced war, natural disasters and the sufferings and injustices of feudalism, but now that the People's Republic of China was established, they no longer faced starvation and their children were able to go to school. The boy's writing expressed the eternal, original purpose of the new China—to liberate the people and bring them happiness. The Chinese people were proud to be moving steadily in that direction.

No country or individual should ever lose sight of their original purpose. It is by constantly returning to our original purpose and challenging ourselves with a fresh spirit that we can achieve new growth and improvement.

SHIN'ICHI AND MINEKO mingled joyfully with the children. They played quoits, a game similar to horseshoe pitching, as well as a popular Chinese board game. They also visited a classroom in which students were building a model airplane. When Shin'ichi greeted one of the boys, who seemed to be enjoying himself as he worked away on the model, the boy said proudly, "When I grow up, I'm going to make a real airplane and fly to Japan."

"Let's meet again when you do," Shin'ichi replied. "And please give me a ride in your plane." The boy smiled as he firmly shook the hand Shin'ichi extended to him.

The children also gave musical and choral performances for the Japanese delegation. Afterward, Shin'ichi said: "I feel completely invigorated by your pure hearts. This has been an unforgettable day. You are all emissaries of the future. You are the treasures of humanity. I'll be sure to tell all my friends in Japan about you."

One girl then said on behalf of her fellow students: "Mr. Yamamoto, we know that you are working very hard for friendship between China and Japan. We want to be friends with the children of Japan. We'll share our meeting with you today with everyone in our school."

Then Shin'ichi and the others left the children's palace, seen off by the smiles and cheers of the young people. Shin'ichi was deeply moved by their vibrancy and purity, a feeling that would stay with him forever. He keenly felt that he had to build strong and lasting ties of friendship between Japan and China for the sake of those children.

He also thought about the deteriorating relations between China and the Soviet Union. What would happen to those children if a war were to break out between these two countries? Peace between them had to be realized for the children's sake. Toward that end, he determined to communicate the feelings of the Chinese people to the Soviets with all his strength and life force. His resolve was fierce. Earnest and sincere actions arising from strong convictions and deep-seated determination can break through any stalemate.

A MISTY RAIN fell in the city of Hangzhou, intensifying the green of its beautiful willows and Chinese parasol trees. On June 12, Shin'ichi and his party visited Hangzhou City, the capital of Zhejiang Province, known as the home of Xi Hu, or West Lake, and for its wonderful silk fabrics. The previous day, after visiting the Children's Palace in Shanghai, they boarded a train at half past seven, arriving in Hangzhou at nearly eleven that night.

During the three hours or so of the journey, Shin'ichi had a lively conversation with China-Japan Friendship

Association Secretary-General Sun Pinghua, who was accompanying the delegation, about the aims of the Soka Gakkai and the future of Japan–China relations. The secretary-general was a friend who understood the Soka Gakkai, but Shin'ichi was intent on helping him gain a deeper, more accurate appreciation of the organization and its present situation.

Given that the circumstances surrounding the Soka Gakkai are constantly changing, it is important to continue engaging people in dialogue so that they will consistently have a correct perception of the organization. It is also crucial to give them a deeper understanding of the Soka Gakkai as a whole.

On the morning of June 12, Shin'ichi and the others visited a silk brocade factory. After receiving an explanation of the production process, they had an opportunity to watch a bolt of fabric, with all its vibrant colors, being woven to completion. The skill and craft involved were truly impressive.

In the afternoon, they visited West Lake, a famous scenic area about 9.3 miles in circumference and surrounded by green mountains. Under rainy skies, the lake lived up to the description of it by the renowned Northern Sung-dynasty poet Su Tung-p'o (Su Dongpo, pen name Su Shih, 1036–1101): "The color of the hills under a drizzly sky—rain too is superb!"[34] After taking a boat ride, they visited Huagang Guanyu Park on the lake's shore. Rain continued to fall, so Shin'ichi and the others took shelter in a rest station in the park together with about twenty other Chinese visitors to the park.

Shin'ichi addressed the Chinese in a friendly manner,

seeing this as a good opportunity to interact with ordinary citizens. When he thought of his purpose in visiting China, he knew that he couldn't waste a single minute. He wanted to speak and form ties of friendship with as many people as possible.

The population of China was said to be eight hundred million. A dialogue with one individual might have seemed a small thing, but just as one drop of water becomes part of a great river, everything starts and develops from one person. That is why each person is so important.

SHIN'ICHI SMILED at a Chinese man also waiting out the rain and said: "I'm visiting from Japan. West Lake is famous for its beauty in Japan as well." The man smiled back and remarked: "The cherry blossoms in Japan are also famous. I've heard that cherry blossom season is very beautiful there." As they exchanged pleasantries, their hearts gradually opened to each other.

"In the interests of Japan–China friendship, then, please allow us to sing you a song about cherry blossoms," Shin'ichi said. He and the members of his delegation thus began to sing "Ohka Ramman no Uta" (Song of Cherry Blossoms): "The cherries are in full bloom, the moon is dim, the butterflies dance..." When the song was over, everyone applauded.

Noticing a boy among the Chinese group, Shin'ichi turned to him and said: "Your generation will play the lead in the twenty-first century. Please study hard and grow into a fine person. And please come to visit Japan some day." When the interpreter communicated Shin'ichi's words to the boy, he smiled shyly and nodded.

Shin'ichi next addressed a Chinese man who, he was told, had worked for many years as a miner, saying: "I know your work requires tremendous strength and must be very demanding, but it's also very important. Please live a long and healthy life. That will be a sign of the victory of the Chinese people."

The man replied cheerfully: "Thank you for your encouragement. Your words are a great inspiration. You take care of yourself, too!"

"Thank you," Shin'ichi said. "Let's remain youthful as long as we live."

The two men smiled and shook hands.

When they left Huagang Guanyu Park, Kaoru Tahara, the Soka Gakkai student division leader and a member of Shin'ichi's party, asked, "Sensei, what's your secret for being able to win people's hearts and offer appropriate words of encouragement wherever you go?"

"There's no secret to it at all," Shin'ichi replied. "I just give each encounter my all. I know that I may never see the person again, so I think about how I can connect deeply with them and pour my whole being into doing so. That earnest commitment manifests itself as wisdom and strength."

SHIN'ICHI AND HIS party returned to Shanghai shortly after ten in the evening on June 12. The next morning, they visited Caoyang New Village, a worker's residential community in Shanghai's Putuo District. It was home to some fifteen thousand working families, with a total of about seventy thousand residents.

Shin'ichi and the others visited one of the day-care

centers and a kindergarten there, where they had fun interacting with the children. To welcome them, the children performed lively songs and dances. Their tiny dancing forms were adorable. In reciprocation, Shin'ichi sat down at the piano and played the Japanese songs, "Haru ga Kita" (Spring Has Come), "Sakura" (Cherry Blossoms) and "Musunde Hiraite" (Close Hands, Open Hands). The children smiled, clapping their hands and moving their heads in time to the music. They made a strong and deep connection with Shin'ichi, whose love for children was apparent to all.

The American poet Henry Wadsworth Longfellow (1807–82) said, "Music is the universal language of mankind."[35]

That afternoon, Shin'ichi and his party visited the

Hongqiao People's Commune. After touring its factory and irrigation system, the delegation met with seven young people who worked there. Shin'ichi asked them directly: "It's my understanding that serving the people is the fundamental educational philosophy of the People's Republic of China. But there must be some young people who aren't interested in that. How do you encourage them to embrace that idea?"

In response, one young man talked about his own experience. "I work on a farm here," he said, "and when I started, I had to carry buckets of soil balanced on a pole, but I couldn't keep my balance and was hardly able to walk. A man who had once been a very poor farmer, however, comforted me, encouraged me and taught me how to do it. I'll never forget his warm encouragement to keep on trying. Through that simple encounter, I learned about human kindness and keenly felt just how great people can be. I thus decided to spend the rest of my life serving the people."

The spirit of serving the people is cultivated by working alongside the people, sharing their joys and sufferings and learning from them.

THE YOUNG MAN continued speaking enthusiastically, "The encouragement of others combined with my own efforts to continue striving without giving up has given me tremendous confidence."

A young woman who was living apart from her parents and was experiencing farm labor for the first time on the commune next related her experience: "At first I was exhausted by the work. My body ached and I could hardly eat, because I was so worn out. As the days went by, I wanted to quit and go back to my parents." She went on to say that she consulted with one of the senior workers, and was consequently able to challenge her weaknesses and become a stronger person. The older woman had shared her own experiences of witnessing people dying of starvation or being massacred before China's liberation. Stressing that they must never allow a return to the days when ordinary people suffered so much, she had also said it was important to endure the struggles of the present in order to build a society that guaranteed the welfare of all Chinese people. The young woman added that the inspiration she received from her more experienced senior enabled her to develop a wish to serve the people.

Human beings can sometimes be extremely vulnerable. If something happens and there is no one there to encourage them, it is easy for people's ideas and beliefs to be shaken. That is why it's important for them to have others around who can inspire and encourage them.

The young woman also said that it was crucial to remember the fundamental reason for the struggle for China's liberation—the terrible suffering and oppression of the people. She further remarked that for the younger generation, having the older generation share their experiences of how people's lives had been prior to the revolution and about the struggle for liberation was a vital factor in establishing the same ideals in their hearts.

When we are able to return to our fundamental starting point, our basic purpose becomes clear, and we feel empowered. Those who have engraved their starting point in their lives are strong.

Nearly a quarter century had then passed since the establishment of the People's Republic of China (in 1949). China had certainly moved dramatically forward in that time, but the younger generation didn't know how terrible things had been before the revolution. If people were to forget the pioneering spirit, the spirit of the revolution, complacency would set in, leading to corruption and degeneration. If that were to happen, the nation's founding ideals would crumble. That is perhaps why China was searching so intently for a method of personal transformation.

Shin'ichi was happy to meet with young people who were brimming with energy and enthusiasm. When youth are vibrantly active, the future is bright.

THE YOUNG PEOPLE from the commune shared their thoughts on a wide variety of subjects, ranging from marriage to their views on labor to the challenges awaiting a society that has achieved material prosperity. It was a very meaningful discussion, both from the perspective of building friendship between the youth of Japan and China and enabling the former to learn more about their neighbor across the sea.

That night (June 13), the Japanese delegation led by Shin'ichi hosted a thank-you banquet at the Jin Jiang Hotel, where they were staying. Soka Gakkai Student Division Leader Kaoru Tahara, who was welcoming the guests as they arrived, exclaimed on the arrival of one young man, "What a surprise to see you here!" The young man was a member of a Chinese youth delegation that had visited Japan four months earlier. A student assembly had been held at the University of Tokyo to welcome the Chinese delegation, and the Soka Gakkai student division had been invited to participate by the executive committee sponsoring the occasion. Mr. Tahara and other student division members had attended and helped give the Chinese visitors a warm welcome.

Mr. Tahara had spoken at the gathering. Basing his talk on Shin'ichi's call for the normalization of Japan–China diplomatic relations, he urged that the two countries never again engage in war against each other; that bilateral development be promoted in a spirit of equality and mutual benefit; and that the students of both nations work together in friendship to promote the peace and prosperity of Asia. Mr. Tahara also exhorted the students on both sides to transcend all political and ideological differences and together advance powerfully forward for the happiness of all humanity. Mr. Tahara had exchanged a firm handshake with this young man at that time, and now they were unexpectedly reunited.

When Shin'ichi called for the normalization of bilateral relations at the Soka Gakkai's 11th Student Division General Meeting in 1968, he envisioned the youth of Japan and China working hand in hand with a mutual pledge for friendship and peace. Observing the happy reunion of these two young men, he felt that his dream was becoming a reality.

A stream eventually becomes a great river. Japan–China friendship was certain to be carried on by the younger generation and become a great and unstoppable current of the times.

The French author Victor Hugo (1802–85) wrote, "A point of light in the distance growing larger moment by moment—that is the future."[36] For the sake of the future, we must light a flame today and raise it high for all to see. It is what we do today that counts.

The evening in Shanghai passed with firm friendships being forged between the Japanese and Chinese youth present.

SHIN'ICHI'S VISIT to China was nearing its end. At noon the following day, June 14, he and his party flew from Shanghai back to Guangzhou. Accompanied by China-Japan Friendship Association Secretary-General Sun Pinghua, the group reached the city a little before three. That evening, they visited the Guangzhou Peasant Movement Training Institute.

The institute, which opened in July 1924, had once served as a driving force of the Chinese revolution. Young people had gone there from all over China to study, and then gone on to become the core of the Chinese peasant movement. Mao Zedong had served as the director of the institute for several months, and Zhou Enlai had also lectured there. The youth had also received military training at the institute, and on returning to their hometowns, they had organized the peasantry and eventually overthrew the old regime. Sadly, many young people had been killed in this struggle.

Shin'ichi was interested in learning what it was that had shaped these ordinary youths into such capable leaders of the revolution. Of course, oppression at the hands of feudal warlords and officials and the terrible suffering of the peasantry in pre-revolutionary China were indisputable factors in fomenting the revolution.

Mao Zedong's room at the institute was very plain,

containing a wooden bed that appeared quite hard. In other words, the movement's top leaders had led lives of spartan simplicity, living and working as equals alongside the young people they led. This doubtlessly forged strong empathy and bonds of shared commitment, causing the youth to devote themselves wholeheartedly to the cause.

When Shin'ichi and his party were shown the dining hall, their guide said, "The cooks made noodles for students from northern China, who customarily preferred noodles to rice, and they also cooked beef for those who belonged to minorities that couldn't eat pork."

These were signs of the warm consideration of the institute's leaders, even amid the demanding training sessions they conducted. The youth must have been moved and grateful for such consideration of their needs, inspiring them to challenge themselves all the harder and become stronger. Such sincere concern is the best way to foster people.

Shin'ichi and his party spent the evening, which was to be their last in China, having dinner with officials from Guangzhou City. Both Shin'ichi and Mineko gave their all to speaking with those at their table. They dedicated themselves to the very end to open a path of friendship for the future.

HAVING COMPLETED his itinerary in China, Shin'ichi took some time to talk with China-Japan Friendship Association Secretary-General Sun Pinghua and three other association representatives at the Guangdong Guest House in Guangzhou (on June 14). Their discussion, which lasted nearly three hours, revolved around different ways of viewing people. Shin'ichi expressed the opinion that it was important to see people as individuals rather than group them into distinct classes and that such thinking was sure to positively contribute to China's future growth and development. As a friend, he wished only for the prosperity of China, and it was from that perspective that he spoke sincerely and openly with his Chinese hosts.

It is by individuals forging bonds of trust and empathy with those they come into contact with that a path of friendship among nations can be opened. It boils down to how deeply we can connect with those in our immediate environment.

Shin'ichi also repeatedly expressed his profound gratitude for the kind hospitality he and his party had received during their visit to China, saying: "Your warm sincerity made every day a deeply moving experience. This has been a very meaningful visit for me. And becoming friends with you has definitely been the highlight."

Our impression of another country is often formed by the people from that country whom we encounter and spend time with. People are what matter.

Lastly, Shin'ichi wrote messages on decorative placards for his Chinese friends to convey his heartfelt gratitude. To Sun Pinghua, he wrote, "Friends forever, come rain or come shine." To Ye Qiyong and Yin Lianyu, who had warmly looked after the Japanese delegation during their visit, he wrote respectively: "This historic visit will be remembered for generations to come" and "A golden bridge linking the hearts of China and Japan." And to the young man Chen Yongchang, who had accompanied them since their arrival in Beijing, he wrote, "Together, walking the path of the people, upholding the banner of friendship."

Then, Sun Pinghua picked up the brush to write his own messages to Shin'ichi and Mineko. Respectively, he wrote: "China–Japan friendship will be as enduring as pine and oak" and "Let us convey our friendship to future generations." He also wrote a message for the entire visiting Japanese delegation, "Serving the people," which he and the three other representatives signed.

"Thank you so much," Shin'ichi said. "This itself is the Soka Gakkai spirit. Let's work together to serve the people of Japan and China and for the sake of the happiness of all humanity." Shin'ichi and Sun Pinghua shook hands firmly.

THE MORNING OF the delegation's departure arrived (June 15), marking a fresh start on a path of everlasting friendship. At eight o'clock, Shin'ichi and his party left the Guangdong Guest House and went to Guangzhou Station, where they bid farewell to China-Japan Friendship Association Secretary-General Sun Pinghua and association member Chen Yongchang, both of whom had been with them since Beijing. Ye Qiyong and Yin Lianyu accompanied the group back to Shenzhen, the starting point of their journey.

Their train arrived at Shenzhen Station, the last railway station in China before the border with Hong Kong, at 10:05 AM. Everyone disembarked, and the Japanese delegation headed for Lo Wu Station on the Hong Kong side. A small river only a few meters wide at its narrowest point marked the border between the People's Republic of China and the British Territory of Hong Kong. Standing on the steel bridge spanning the river, the group said goodbye to Mr. Ye and Ms. Yin. Shin'ichi remarked: "Thank you so much for everything. I'll never forget what you've done for us. Our friendship is eternal. Let's meet again. Please come to Japan." Shin'ichi shook hands vigorously with both of them, and he hugged Mr. Ye while Mineko hugged Ms. Yin. The two young interpreters then shook hands with the rest of the delegation. It was a lingering farewell.

Shin'ichi smiled and said in Chinese: "Thank you! Let's meet again!"

With that, the group began walking away. Mr. Ye and Ms. Yin watched them leave with tears in their eyes, waving until they were out of sight. Shin'ichi and the others also turned around and waved again and again, calling out, "See you again soon!" It was an image of true friendship.

As he made his way across the border, Shin'ichi deeply pledged to himself: "For the sake of my Chinese friends, I will do everything I can to prevent war between China and the Soviet Union. My next trip must be to the Soviet Union!" A fresh fighting spirit to establish peace between the two countries blazed brightly in his heart.

The British historian Arnold J. Toynbee (1889–1975), with whom Shin'ichi had conducted a dialogue, said of his approach to work: "I would start work on the next item on the very day on which I had finished work on what had now just ceased to be the current item. I never paused to take a breath."[37] Such a spirit is crucial if great things are to be achieved.

Before the start of Shin'ichi's trip, Dr. Toynbee had sent him a message warmly applauding his upcoming China visit.

WHEN THE TRAIN from Lo Wu Station carrying Shin'ichi and his party made its next stop at Sheungshui Station, several people came running down the platform, looking in the windows. It was the leader of the Soka Gakkai organization in Hong Kong, Chou Chi Kong, and other members. Sheung Shui Station was the closest station to the border with China where Hong Kong residents didn't need a permit to board and disembark from the train. When Shin'ichi and Mineko noticed Mr. Chou and the others, they opened their window and waved to them.

"Sensei!" cried the group outside as they boarded the

train. Mr. Chou's face was drenched with perspiration. Smiling broadly, he said: "Welcome back! Congratulations on the great success of your visit to China!"

The Hong Kong members knew all about Shin'ichi's trip from copies of the *Seikyo Shimbun*, the Soka Gakkai newspaper, sent to them from Japan.

"Thank you for coming to see us," Shin'ichi said. "We were able to open a path of friendship. I will do everything I possibly can for the sake of all of you here in Hong Kong and for the peace and prosperity of China."

Mr. Chou was deeply touched by Shin'ichi's warm concern for them.

As the train journey commenced, Shin'ichi took out a sheet of paper and began to write. Since the final days of his seventeen-day visit to China, he had been writing in his spare time. Several newspapers and magazines had asked him before his departure to write articles about his impressions of China. His schedule after returning to Japan was very tight, and he also knew that if he wrote sympathetically or positively about China, he would surely be criticized. Aware of all of this, however, he enthusiastically accepted the requests, wanting to enable as many people as possible to learn more about China and gain a deeper understanding of the country and its people.

The present moment is crucial in determining future success. That is why Shin'ichi was always sincere and in earnest, and why he gave his full energies to everything he did.

He wrote enough to fill a book after his return from China. Eventually, it was compiled and published as

Chugoku no ningen kakumei (*The Human Revolution in China*).

At the banquet he had hosted in Beijing (on June 6), Shin'ichi said with regard to his determination to see friendship forged with China: "These are not just empty words to me. Please watch our future actions!" He thus embarked on a wholehearted effort to fulfill his promise and realize everlasting peace and friendship between Japan and China.

Notes:

1. Translated from Chinese. *Lu Xun quanji* (Collected Works of Lu Xun) (Beijing: Renmin Wenxue Chubanshe, 1996), vol. 3, p. 256.

2. Translated from Japanese. Sun Yat-sen, *Son Bun senshu* (Selected Writings of Sun Yat-sen), translated by Yozo Hayashi and edited by Yoshitsugu Ichiji and Ichiro Yamaguchi (Tokyo: Shakai Shiso-sha, 1987), vol. 2, p. 308.

3. According to Chinese government figures from 1995.

4. Miguel de Cervantes Saavedra, *The Adventures of Don Quixote,* translated by J. M. Cohen (London: Penguin Books, 1950), p. 801.

5. H. G. Wells, *The Outline of History: Being a Plain History of Life and Mankind* (New York: P. F. Collier & Son Company, 1922), vol. 4, p. 1290.

6. John Emerich Edward Dalberg-Acton, *Essays on Freedom and Power* (Boston: The Beacon Press, 1949), p. 364.

7. Zhou Enlai, *Selected Works of Zhou Enlai* (Beijing: Foreign Languages Press, 1989), vol. 2, p. 205.

8. Translated from Japanese. *Jogan seiyo* (The Essentials of Government in the Chen-kuan Era), vol.1, translated by Taneshige Harada, in *Shinshaku kambun taikei* (A New Compendium

of Chinese Classics) (Tokyo: Meiji Shoin, 1978), vol. 95, p. 619.

9. Both the junior high and high schools in Tokyo and Osaka went coeducational in 1982.

10. Victor Hugo, *Les Misérables*, translated by Lee Fahnestock and Norman MacAfee (New York: New American Library, 1987), p. 650.

11. Translated from Chinese. Liao Chengzhi, *Liao Chengzhi wenji* (Liao Chengzhi Writings) (Hong Kong: Joint Publishing Co., 1990), vol. 1, p. 127.

12. Lu Xun, "Shanghai Children," in *Selected Works*, translated by Yang Xianyi and Gladys Yang (Beijing: Foreign Language Press, 1985), vol. 3, p. 334.

13. Translated from French. Jules Michelet, *L'Étudiant* (Paris: Éditions du Seuil, 1970), p. 99.

14. Marcus Tullius Cicero, *On the Good Life*, translated by Michael Grant (New York: Penguin Books, 1971), p. 185.

15. Jean-Jacques Rousseau, *Emile*, or *On Education*, translated by Allan Bloom (London: Penguin Books, 1991), p. 390.

16. Albert Einstein, *Einstein on Peace*, edited by Otto Nathan and Heinz Norden (New York: Avenel Books, 1981), p. 126.

17. Translated from Japanese. Haribhau Upadhaya, *Bapu monogatari* (The Story of Bapu), translated from Hindi by Hakobu Ikeda (Tokyo: Kodansha Shuppan Sabisu Senta, 1998), p. 22.

18. T'ien-t'ai's three major works: *Great Concentration and Insight, Profound Meaning of the Lotus Sutra,* and *Words and Phrases of the Lotus Sutra.*

19. John Dewey, *Lectures in China, 1919–1920,* translated and edited from Chinese by Robert W. Clopton and Tsiun-Chen Ou (Honolulu: The University Press of Hawaii, 1973), p. 185.

20. Rabindranath Tagore, *Of Myself,* translated from Bengali by Devadatta Joardar and Joe Winter (London: Anvil Press Poetry, 2006), p. 85.

21. Ralph Waldo Emerson, "The American Scholar," in *Essays and Lectures* (New York: Library of America, 1983), p. 60.

22. Thomas Carlyle, *On Heroes, Hero-Worship, and the Heroic in History,* edited by Carl Niemeyer (Lincoln, Nebraska: University of Nebraska Press, 1966), p. 45.

23. Five Principles of Peaceful Coexistence: Series of agreements drawn up between China and India in 1954, which continue to serve as fundamental guidelines for China in fostering and developing friendly relations with other nations. They are: (1) mutual respect for territorial integrity and sovereignty, (2) mutual nonaggression, (3) mutual noninterference in internal affairs, (4) equality and mutual benefit and (5) peaceful coexistence.

24. Translated from German. Richard Nikolaus Coudenhove-Kalergi, "Wahrheitsliebe" (Love of Truth), *Ethik und hyperethik* (Leipzig: Neue Geist-Verlag, 1923), p. 48.

25. Translated from Japanese. Zhou Enlai, *Shu Onrai senshu* (Selected Writings of Zhou Enlai), translated and edited by Shuichi Morishita (Tokyo: Chugoku Shoten, 1978), vol. 2, p. 1108.

26. Marco Polo Bridge Incident: Also known as the Lugouqiao Incident. A skirmish between Chinese and Japanese troops on the outskirts of Beiping (now Beijing).

27. Ellen Key, *Love and Marriage,* translated by Arthur G. Chater (New York: G. P. Putnam's Sons, 1911), p. 260.

28. Lu Xun, "Reply to Xu Maoyong and on the Question of the United Front Against Japanese Aggression," in *Selected Works,* translated by Yang Xianyi and Gladys Yang (Beijing: Foreign Language Press, 1985), vol. 4, pp. 299–300.

29. Lu Xun, "Preface to *Call to Arms,*" in *Selected Works,* translated by Yang Xianyi and Gladys Yang (Beijing: Foreign Language Press, 1985), vol. 1, p. 35.

30. Lu Xun, "Preface to *Call to Arms,*" in *Selected Works*, p. 35.

31. Translated from Chinese. Lu Xun, *Lu Xun quanji* (The Complete Works of Lu Xun) (Beijing: Renmin Wenxue Chubanshe, 1996), vol. 11, p. 249.

32. Marcus Aurelius, *Meditations,* translated by Maxwell Staniforth (London: Penguin Books, 1964), p. 126.

33. Israel Epstein, *Woman in World History: Life and Times of Soong Ching Ling (Mme. Sun Yatsen)* (Beijing: New World Press, 1993), p. 535.

34. Su Tung-p'o, *Selected Poems of Su Tung-p'o,* translated by Burton Watson (Port Townsend, Washington: Copper Canyon Press, 1994), p. 49.

35. Henry Wadsworth Longfellow, *Outre-Mer: A Pilgrimage Beyond the Sea* (Boston: Ticknor and Fields, 1856), p. 202.

36. Translated from French. Victor Hugo, *Pendant l'exil 1852–1870,* in *Actes et paroles* (Paris: Albin Michel, 1938), vol. 2, p. 173.

37. Arnold Toynbee, *Experiences* (New York: Oxford University Press, 1969), p. 113.

Bridge Building

W ITH LIGHT hearts, let's take a fresh step forward. Life is a struggle against the limits of time. We must therefore strive to make each day one of ceaseless advancement. The great Russian poet Aleksandr Pushkin wrote:

> Thou art a king and kings must live alone.
> Thine own free spirit calls
> to thee; pass on,
> Make perfect the fair
> blossom of thy dreams,
> Nor ask for praises of achievement won.[1]

These words mirrored Shin'ichi Yamamoto's personal determination. He had deeply resolved to dedicate his life to the realization of peace for the sake of all humanity.

On September 8, 1974, Shin'ichi flew to the Soviet Union at the invitation of Moscow State University. It was his first visit there. He departed from Tokyo's Haneda International Airport a little after eleven that morning. Shin'ichi was scheduled to spend ten days in the Soviet Union, visiting Moscow and Leningrad (present-day Saint Petersburg), with official visits to Moscow State University, the Union of Soviet Societies for Friendship and Cultural Relations with Foreign Countries, the Soviet Ministries of Culture and Education, and Leningrad State University (present-day Saint Petersburg State University). He was accompanied by his wife, Mineko, the president of Soka University and a faculty member, Soka Gakkai youth division and women's division representatives, a *Seikyo Shimbun* reporter and photographer, and a videographer—making for a party of eleven in all. The purpose of the visit was to engage in educational and cultural exchange in an effort to promote friendship and deepen mutual understanding toward the realization of peace.

Relations between nations ultimately come down to relations between individuals. In order to establish true and lasting friendly bilateral relations, ties of friendship and trust must first be forged between the individuals living in each country. As such, Shin'ichi believed it was crucial to encourage interaction on the private, individual level more than the official, political level.

Another goal of his visit was to communicate to the

Soviet leadership that China did not want war. He was firmly resolved to make efforts to ensure that military confrontation between the Soviet Union and the People's Republic of China was avoided. He was also determined to initiate steps that would steer the United States and the Soviet Union, as well as a world divided into opposing Western and Eastern blocs, in the direction of harmony and peace.

SHIN'ICHI'S TRIP to the Soviet Union became a possibility following a meeting on December 7, 1973, with Aleksei Narochnitskii and Maksim Kim, members of the Academy of Sciences of the Soviet Union.

At the time, relations between Japan and the Soviet Union were beginning to thaw, but various obstacles still remained. The two countries had normalized their diplomatic relations in 1956, but when Japan signed the new Japan–U.S. Security Treaty in 1960, it cast a chill over the country's relations with the Soviet Union. The Soviet Union adopted the position that the issue of disputed sovereignty over several small islands located northeast of the Japanese archipelago had been resolved, and it refused to even discuss the possibility of their return to Japan. It also continued to apprehend Japanese fishing boats in the waters around those islands.

In October 1973, Japanese Prime Minister Kakuei Tanaka made an official visit to the Soviet Union and met with Soviet General Secretary Leonid Brezhnev. It was the first meeting between top-level leaders of the two nations in seventeen years. It seemed as if events were moving in the direction of a peace treaty, but the future remained shrouded in a fog of uncertainty and mutual suspicion.

Exchange between nations on the political and economic levels is often disrupted or derailed by national self-interests. That is why Shin'ichi continued to emphasize the importance of broad-ranging cultural, educational and academic exchange on the private level in order to establish lasting bilateral peace and friendship. With this conviction, he strove to bring about cultural exchange between Japan and the Soviet Union. In 1966, the Soka Gakkai-affiliated Min-On Concert Association invited the Soviet National Academy Novosibirsk Ballet to perform in Japan. As the founder of Min-On, Shin'ichi worked very hard behind the scenes to realize this plan.

Soviet leaders, too, began to take note of Shin'ichi and the Soka Gakkai, recognizing the organization as a newly emerging force of the people in Japan. In 1963, the editorial department of *Asia and Africa Today*, a journal published by a research institution affiliated with the Academy of Sciences of the Soviet Union, invited Soka Gakkai youth division representatives to visit the Soviet Union. In 1967, the Soviet minister to Japan and other embassy personnel attended the Soka Gakkai's Tokyo Culture Festival, held at the National Stadium in Tokyo. The following year, in order to gain a deeper understanding of the Soka Gakkai, the Soviet ambassador visited the head temple, Taiseki-ji.

IN THE AUTUMN of 1973, the Japan Cultural Association, a nongovernmental body promoting Japan–Soviet exchange, together with another organization, sent out feelers to see if Shin'ichi would be interested in visiting the Soviet Union. The Soviet official in charge of relations with Japan hoped that the Soka Gakkai might serve as a new bridge for exchange between the two nations, whose relations were chilly. Shin'ichi replied that he would indeed be willing to visit the Soviet Union to promote bilateral cultural exchange and contribute to building lasting peace.

After that, the Japan Cultural Association forwarded a request to Shin'ichi. A symposium on the history of Japan and the Soviet Union would be held in Tokyo in December, and Soviet historians would be attending. The historians wished to visit Soka University, and it was hoped that they could also meet with the university's founder, Shin'ichi, on that occasion. Though Soka University was only three years old at the time, it seemed that the Soviet academics were very interested in this new institution that aimed to become an unsurpassed citadel of humanistic education.

The Japan Cultural Association staff was making a concerted effort to encourage exchange between the Soka Gakkai and the Soviet Union. They had high hopes that the Soka Gakkai and Shin'ichi might play a central role in Japan–Soviet exchange from now on. Shigeyoshi Matsumae, president of Tokai University, was the president of the Japan Cultural Association, and as a university head, he had apparently been watching Soka University's development with close interest.

When Shin'ichi learned that Soviet historians wished to visit Soka University and meet with him there, he immediately consulted with the school's president and other faculty members. "I hope that they will talk not only with me but also with students and professors," he said. "I am certain that this chance to interact with Soviet academics across ideological and political barriers will be a precious experience in the lives of our Soka University students, young people who will be active in the twenty-first century. It's a very important opportunity. Why doesn't the university officially invite the academics and request that they deliver a special lecture for the students?"

Shin'ichi wished to provide Soka University students with many opportunities to learn and grow.

AFTER SHIN'ICHI'S discussion with the president and some faculty members of Soka University, it was decided to send an official invitation to the Soviet scholars. On December 6 and 7, Aleksei Narochnitskii and Maksim Kim of the Soviet Union's Academy of Sciences visited Soka University. On December 6, Mr. Narochnitskii delivered a lecture on "Issues Related to Peace and Security in the International Policy of the Soviet Union," and on the following day, Mr. Kim spoke on "The Present State of Cultural Development of the Peoples of the Soviet Union." After the presentation December 7, the Soviet academics met and talked with Shin'ichi as well as the Soka University president, the board of trustees' chair and faculty representatives.

At this meeting, Shin'ichi made four suggestions. These were a result of his thinking seriously about what could best be done, from the Soviet Union's position, to improve bilateral relations and realize peace.

The first was the establishment of an organization,

provisionally called the Japan-Soviet Students Cultural Exchange Association, which would promote relations between students of the two nations.

The second was the establishment of a United Nations of Education Headquarters in Moscow. The United Nations of Education, as envisaged by Shin'ichi, would be an international alliance committed to protecting the independence of educational rights that would serve as a spiritual citadel dedicated to world peace. Shin'ichi first proposed this United Nations of Education in a message he sent to an American Soka Gakkai student division general meeting held in October 1973.

His third proposal was the establishment of a course in Buddhist philosophy and Eastern thought at Moscow State University. Without studying and gaining a deeper understanding of the philosophies that served as the spiritual foundations of Asian peoples, it would be difficult for Soviet citizens to connect with their Asian counterparts. Nor would it be possible to realize world peace.

His final proposal was the construction of a Buddhist temple in the Soviet Union. Explaining this idea, Shin'ichi said: "To be honest, most Japanese people don't have a very favorable impression of the Soviet Union. They regard it as an intolerant, ideological nation that doesn't recognize freedom of religion. This works to the disadvantage of the Soviet Union." It was an extremely straightforward remark, and the Japanese woman who was interpreting for Shin'ichi remained silent for quite some time, looking inquiringly at him.

Shin'ichi's credo was perfectly described by Plato's words, "I never hesitate or am ashamed to speak the truth."[2]

THE INTERPRETER was concerned whether she should convey Shin'ichi's words to the Soviet academics exactly as he had spoken them. Realizing this, Shin'ichi said to her: "Please don't worry. Just translate what I've said directly."

He then continued with greater emphasis: "An oppressive, domineering attitude alienates people. It's very important for the Soviet Union to win the sympathy and understanding of Japan and the rest of the world. To do that, it must show tolerance. But words alone cannot convince others of your country's tolerance and open-mindedness. One clear action is far more convincing than a million words. That is the thinking behind my proposal to build a Buddhist temple in the Soviet Union. It would show that the Soviet Union is tolerant of religion and would convince many Japanese people and others around the world that your country respects individual spiritual freedom. I believe that such a move would have tremendous significance, starting with it being an important step toward winning the trust of other countries."

After listening to Shin'ichi's four proposals, Aleksei Narochnitskii said: "Thank you for your ideas. We'll take them into consideration." He and Maksim Kim seemed impressed by Shin'ichi's straightforward manner and opinions.

With great feeling, Mr. Kim said, "I believe that you are a historic leader who embodies creative principles that people today are seeking."

Two days later, before returning to their country, the academics expressed a personal wish to see a visit by Shin'ichi to Moscow State University realized, saying that they would do everything possible to ensure that it happened. Thus, a further step was taken toward Shin'ichi visiting the Soviet Union.

A lively debate had been going on in Moscow over whether or not to extend an invitation to Shin'ichi. Ivan Kovalenko, vice president of the Soviet-Japan Society and the person in charge of matters related to Japan in the International Department of the Central Committee of the Communist Party of the Soviet Union, later wrote in an article for the *Seikyo Shimbun* about the process leading up to Shin'ichi's invitation.[3] According to the article, at the outset, most Communist Party officials opposed inviting Shin'ichi, because they lacked correct information about the Soka Gakkai.

MR. KOVALENKO had taken note of Shin'ichi and the Soka Gakkai from early on and had worked together with Soviet embassy staff in Japan to collect information on both. He had also met directly with Hisaya Yamamichi, who was public relations director and also a vice president of the Soka Gakkai, and learned a great deal about the organization. As a result, he had a high opinion of the Soka Gakkai and called for active exchange to be initiated with it. But many Soviet officials knew very little about either Shin'ichi or the Soka Gakkai, causing their view of both to be rather superficial.

There was also the question of whether there could be any common ground between the Soka Gakkai, a religious organization, and the Soviet government, which, as a Marxist-Leninist state, rejected religion. Shin'ichi had also spoken out for the normalization of relations between Japan and the People's Republic of China, with which the Soviet Union was experiencing tensions. Many people concerned in the matter were suspicious of Shin'ichi on that point alone. A majority of them felt that a decision on whether to invite Shin'ichi or not should await a more thorough investigation of him and the Soka Gakkai's aims and philosophy.

Mr. Kovalenko, however, continued to urge that Shin'ichi be invited to the country. He felt it was a question of crucial importance whether the ten-million-strong Soka Gakkai became an ally and a new bridge linking the Soviet Union and Japan or whether it took a negative stance toward the Soviet Union. Having a solid grasp of the situation in Asia, he also keenly recognized that Shin'ichi and the Soka Gakkai were working hard to ease tensions between Japan and China and to strengthen those countries' relations.

Mr. Kovalenko had been the editor of a newspaper published for Japanese prisoners of war held by the Soviets after World War II and was one of the Soviet Union's leading experts on Japan. He was also feared as a man of iron principles. He was known for his firm and assertive approach to relations with Japan and was criticized by some for his intimidating diplomatic stance. Yet this very Mr. Kovalenko was insisting that President Yamamoto be invited to the Soviet Union to meet with top officials and given a full diplomatic welcome. Eventually, his passionate advocacy won over the Communist Party's Politburo and Soviet Premier Aleksey Kosygin.

THE SOVIET UNION weighed the matter of inviting Shin'ichi to the country carefully. He was, after all, the president of the Soka Gakkai and a religious leader, while the Soviet Union was a socialist state. The consensus was that it would be problematic for the Communist Party to extend the invitation. It was thus decided that Moscow State University would do so, based on the fact that Shin'ichi was also the founder of Soka University.

On December 21, 1973, two weeks after the historians from the Academy of Sciences of the Soviet Union had visited Soka University, the Great Siberian Fair opened at a stadium in Tokyo. The fair introduced Siberia's natural environment, culture, history and present state of development, and among the many exhibits was a reconstruction of a woolly mammoth. The Soviet government and the Japan Cultural Association had devoted a great deal of energy to the fair, hoping to deepen understanding of the Soviet Union among Japanese people.

But on January 21, 1974, just a month after the fair opened, the pavilion air dome in which the exhibition was being housed collapsed under the weight of the winter snow, and part of the exhibition was destroyed. The damage was considerable, and the fair was closed for about six weeks to undergo repairs. Shin'ichi, who had also hoped that the event would contribute to improved bilateral relations, was deeply disappointed by this unfortunate occurrence. As a result, when individuals involved in organizing the fair contacted him, he decided to offer the Soka Gakkai's cooperation and support.

Up to that time, Shin'ichi had made various efforts to promote friendly relations between the two countries, including inviting the Soviet National Academy Novosibirsk Ballet to Japan under the auspices of the Min-On

Concert Association, which he founded. He wasn't concerned about what people would think. His actions were based solely on his strong personal convictions. As the Russian writer Maksim Gorky wrote, "A soul with integrity never wavers."[4]

In April 1974, an invitation for Shin'ichi to visit the Soviet Union arrived from Rector Rem Khokhlov of Moscow State University. In May, Shin'ichi met and talked with Russian Ambassador to Japan Oleg Troyanovskii at the Seikyo Shimbun Building in Tokyo. On that occasion, Shin'ichi entrusted the ambassador with his letter of acceptance for the invitation from the university. His visit to the Soviet Union was thus finally scheduled for autumn of that year.

At the end of May, Shin'ichi embarked on his first visit to the People's Republic of China. In his heart, he resolved to become a bridge of friendship linking China and the Soviet Union.

AFTER HE HAD returned to Japan from his visit to China, Shin'ichi spoke with the members who would be accompanying him on his trip to the Soviet Union. He said: "The reason I'm traveling to the Soviet Union is that I want to do whatever I can to prevent a third world war. That's why I am going there after my visit to China, and then I will go to the United States. As an emissary of Nichiren Daishonin, I'm going equipped with a philosophy of peace and reverence for life, determined to raise the curtain on an age of world peace.

"A great challenge for the sake of peace awaits us, and we must not fail. We have to act with courage and resolve in order to create change. We cannot succeed if we are hesitant or timid." Shin'ichi's words were filled with fierce determination.

Preparations for his visit to the Soviet Union proceeded at a steady pace, but actually very few people supported his decision to go there. Even Soka Gakkai Vice President Kiyoshi Jujo and other top Soka Gakkai leaders opposed the trip.

At a certain Nichiren Shoshu temple in Tokyo, the resident priest said scornfully to a women's division leader, "Why is Mr. Yamamoto going to an atheist country where no one practices Buddhism?" There was no way that people like this priest, who had no awareness of their mission as Buddhists to work for world peace, could understand what Shin'ichi was trying to do.

A leader of the Japanese business world, concerned for Shin'ichi, also pleaded earnestly with him, saying: "The socialist nations are destined to reach a dead end. Promoting friendship with them is useless. You should give up your plans to visit the Soviet Union. Why is it that you're so determined to go there and to other countries like it in the first place?"

While he appreciated the man's concern, Shin'ichi replied plainly: "Because there are fellow human beings living there. I'm going there to meet people. Whether a country is socialist or capitalist, people who want peace live there. I'm making this trip to build bridges of friendship linking people's hearts, because I firmly believe that is the surest way to achieve peace." Shin'ichi spoke fearlessly and with utter conviction.

Impressed by Shin'ichi's words, the business leader

nodded deeply in agreement. "I see you've thought very carefully about this. I admire your determination, and I pray that your visit may be a great success."

SHIN'ICHI'S PLANE landed in Moscow shortly after three in the afternoon on September 8. This was the day on which, in 1957, second Soka Gakkai president Josei Toda had delivered his Declaration for the Abolition of Nuclear Weapons—his most vital injunction to the youth—at a youth division sports festival held at the Mitsuzawa Stadium in Yokohama. It was also on September 8, 1968, that Shin'ichi had proposed the normalization of diplomatic relations between Japan and China at a student division general meeting held at the Nihon University Auditorium in Ryogoku, Tokyo. Now, September 8 was to also mark the day when Shin'ichi first set foot in the Soviet Union, the leader of the Eastern Bloc and also one of the major nuclear powers. He was making this visit out of his determination to create a bridge between the Soviet Union and China, with which he had been able to forge a path of exchange as a result of his 1968 declaration.

As he stood at the top of the stairs at the entrance of the plane and gazed up at the clear skies over Moscow, Shin'ichi envisioned the face of his mentor, Josei Toda, and made a profound pledge: "Sensei! I have come to the Soviet Union to share your philosophy of world peace and the ideal of Buddhist humanism in an effort to open the way to peace!"

Those who cherish their mentor in their hearts are strong. A mentor in life is a source of courage and inspiration.

In a display of the Russian side's goodwill, Moscow State University Rector Rem Khokhlov, Vice Rector Vladimir Tropin, Deputy Vice Rector Leonid Kharyukov and Leon Strijak, a senior lecturer of Japanese at the university who was to act as interpreter, were waiting on the tarmac to greet Shin'ichi and his traveling companions. Representatives of the Union of Soviet Societies of Friendship and Cultural Relations With Foreign Countries and the Soviet-Japan Society were present as well. The faces of the welcome party were somewhat serious and tense. They seemed uncertain how to go about greeting Shin'ichi, a Buddhist leader.

Sensing their feelings, Shin'ichi smiled brightly and said: "Thank you all for coming out to meet us. Your tireless efforts have made it possible for me to realize my long-cherished dream of visiting Moscow. I've come here to learn from you. I plan to study hard while I'm here, so please regard me as your student and teach me everything you can."

Shin'ichi's words brought smiles to the faces of all there.

SHIN'ICHI FIRMLY shook Rector Khokhlov's hand. "I've been looking forward to meeting you," he said enthusiastically. "Compared to the long tradition and history of Moscow State University, Soka University is like a grandchild. But we would like to grow into a university that can work together with yours toward the realization of world peace in the twenty-first century."

After Shin'ichi's words had been interpreted, Rector Khokhlov indicated his approval. It seemed that he really appreciated Shin'ichi's passionate commitment to education. Shaking Shin'ichi's hand vigorously, he replied, "I've been very eager to meet you, Mr. Yamamoto, as the founder of a new Japanese university dedicated to peace for all humanity."

Rector Khokhlov was forty-eight, just two years older than Shin'ichi. He was an eminent scientist and a recipient of the Soviet Union's prestigious Lenin Prize, bestowed upon leading individuals in such fields as science, technology and the arts.

Shin'ichi said: "Thank you for your kind words. I have long wished to speak with you. Please share your educational philosophy with me. I hope we can talk extensively, for the sake of peace and humanity's future."

Turning to the rest of the gathering who had come to greet him and his party, Shin'ichi smiled as he shook hands with each of them and said, "I'm so happy to be able to meet so many new friends in the Soviet Union."

Shin'ichi's bright smile and the exchange of conversation lightened the mood. A smile has the power to open people's hearts, put them at ease and bring them together. By the time they boarded the bus, they were all chatting and laughing together like they were old friends. All the barriers fell away as they talked to one another.

Rector Khokhlov said joyfully: "Moscow is at the height of its golden autumn right now. It's the most pleasant season. I'm glad you could come at this time of year."

The Russian writer Fyodor Dostoyevsky remarked that the start of any enterprise is always crucial, the final outcome being largely decided in the initial moments.[5]

AFTER CONTINUING their conversation with Moscow State University Rector Rem Khokhlov

and the others in a guest room at the airport, Shin'ichi and his party went to their lodgings at the Hotel Rossia. A police car with its siren blaring led the motorcade of black cars. As they drove, Moscow State University Vice Rector Vladimir Tropin spoke about the buildings they passed and Moscow's history. Senior Lecturer Leon Strijak interpreted these remarks into fluent Japanese.

Moscow was a beautiful city. The trees, just coming into their fall colors, swayed gently in the breeze, as if performing a melody of peace. After about a forty-minute drive, they arrived at the hotel. It was a large, modern building with more than three thousand rooms. From the windows in his room, Shin'ichi could see the Kremlin surrounded by its red brick walls, as well as Saint Basil's Cathedral, now a museum, with its trademark onion dome.

As soon as they finished unpacking, Shin'ichi and

Mineko sat down and chanted Nam-myoho-renge-kyo. They believed that everything started with prayer and based all their actions on that. Prayer is a kind of pledge; it is based on one's firm resolve. Though they kept their voices low, they chanted in complete earnest. They were praying for the happiness and peace of the Russian people and that someday Bodhisattvas of the Earth would emerge and be active here.

Nichiren Daishonin writes, "If one can move Shakyamuni Buddha, the lord of teachings, can the grass and trees fail to respond, can the waters remain calm" (WND-2, 811). In other words, as long as we base ourselves on the Mystic Law, the foundation of all existence, we can change anything.

At half past six that evening, Shin'ichi and his party attended a welcome banquet hosted by a group of ten Russian officials, including Rector Khoklov, which was held in a restaurant in the hotel where they were staying.

Standing up to deliver opening remarks, the rector said: "Today is a special day for the Soviet Union, for we have the honor of welcoming a great social activist from Japan, Mr. Shin'ichi Yamamoto, and his friends. We are very much aware of Mr. Yamamoto's activities and ideas. The people of the Soviet Union have a profound understanding of and sympathy for the activities of the Soka Gakkai. We are particularly struck by the organization's commitment to peace and the passion for education that is embodied by Soka University."

Those traveling with Shin'ichi were astonished at Rector Khokhlov's words.

THE MEMBERS of Shin'ichi's party were deeply impressed that Rector Khokhlov, whom they had just met, knew so much about President Yamamoto and the Soka Gakkai movement, as well as Soka University.

In reality, however, there was nothing particularly unusual about the fact that the Soviet Union was aware of the Soka Gakkai and had researched it. The lay Buddhist organization had been built virtually from scratch after World War II and, by 1951, when Josei Toda was inaugurated as the Soka Gakkai's second president, its active membership was no more than three thousand. Yet in a mere two decades, it had grown into one of the largest religious organizations in Japan. Furthermore, it had brought together ordinary Japanese citizens into a major grassroots movement striving energetically to improve society and make positive contributions in such fields as culture, education and government. This was a remarkable achievement, deservedly hailed as a modern miracle.

Considering their own concern with tapping the full potential of the people in order to promote the growth and development of their country, it was only natural that Soviet leaders should take a great interest in the Soka Gakkai and its leader, President Yamamoto.

Shin'ichi did his utmost each day to further the development of the Soka Gakkai, encouraging members wholeheartedly and struggling with all his might. The result was the unprecedented growth of the Soka Gakkai. But those traveling with him had come to take his struggles and the significant strides made by the Soka Gakkai for granted. That's why they were surprised that Rector

Khokhlov and other Soviet leaders should be aware of the organization.

The rector closed his remarks, saying: "I am overjoyed to have this opportunity to discuss education with President Yamamoto for the sake of the future of humanity in the twenty-first century. I'd like to make a toast now to the start of our new friendship." After the toast, Shin'ichi delivered words, expressing his deep appreciation for the heartwarming welcome they had received and speaking briefly of the Soka Gakkai. He said: "The Soka Gakkai is the largest organization in Japan created through the initiative of the people. Our greatest focus is peace and the happiness of humanity."

SHIN'ICHI SPOKE with emphasis: "Education is the font of wisdom that will bring peace and enrichment to the twenty-first century. In that context, initiating fruitful educational exchange with your nation, starting from this visit, is a great source of joy to us. And nothing could make us happier than to be able to form friendships with people from various sectors of Soviet society."

Thinking of the future, Shin'ichi then shared his personal determination: "The light shining from people's homes during the beautiful Siberian winter exudes a human warmth that touches those who see it. Similarly, we are resolved to cherish the light that shines in people's hearts across all social and political barriers.

"And just as spring brings the emergence of fresh green sprouts from Siberia's frozen soil, I believe that the future will bring a fresh spring of brighter hope to humanity."

After the greetings were finished, a friendly conversation ensued among everyone over dinner. Shin'ichi stated his views clearly: "Building bridges of friendship requires looking one hundred or two hundred years hence and paving the way forward for future generations. That's why I place tremendous importance on educational exchange. I am convinced that a rising momentum toward world peace can be realized through the creation of lasting exchange, free from the vagaries of political and economic influences, that links not only Japan and the Soviet Union but all the nations of the world."

Shin'ichi's far-reaching vision stemmed from the philosophy of Buddhist humanism that he upheld. He also spoke of his idea for a United Nations of Education. Rector Khokhlov expressed a strong interest in this proposal, calling it a fascinating and important idea. The discussion grew impassioned as the Soviet hosts also spoke about their nation's educational policies.

By the time Shin'ichi started to eat the ice cream that was served as dessert, it had melted. He made a joke: "It looks like the passion of our discussion melted the ice cream! Now, it's a Soviet soft drink!" The crowd broke out laughing. Shin'ichi's humor warmed their hearts even further.

SITUATED ATOP a forested hill, the main building of Moscow State University was a gleaming white, thirty-two-story spired edifice soaring majestically skyward. It was a true palace of learning. On September 9, Shin'ichi and his party visited the university for the first time. The leaves of the birch and linden trees encircling the campus were just beginning to turn a golden yellow, and the flower beds were aglow with red and yellow flowers. A gentle breeze blew, creating a lovely autumnal atmosphere.

The Russian university's full name is M. V. Lomonosov Moscow State University, after the Russian scientist Mikhail Lomonosov, who founded it in 1755, when the country was under czarist rule. Today, it is the nation's largest and most prestigious university.

M. V. Lomonosov is renowned for his achievements not only in physics, chemistry and astronomy, but also as a brilliant linguist and poet. He was born in November 1711, into a fishing family that lived on the coast of the White Sea in the north of Russia. When he was nineteen, he moved to Moscow, where he worked his way through school. He then went to study in Germany. After returning to Russia, he became a member of the St. Petersburg Imperial Academy of Sciences, making great accomplishments as a scientist. Eventually, he began to lay plans to establish a university in Moscow, out of his hope to see legions of young Platos and Newtons emerge from the soil of his homeland. Having himself been forced to undergo considerable hardship to pursue his studies, he proposed a university that would be open to people of all classes in Russian society, nobility and commoners alike. He firmly believed that university education should not be restricted to a privileged few.

Mr. Lomonosov worked diligently to make the preparations for launching the university. During the czarist period, with its highly stratified society, establishing an institute of higher education open to all people was a daunting challenge. He faced many difficulties in the effort to receive the necessary permissions from the Russian Senate. Only when the cooperation of the high-ranking minister Ivan Shuvalov, a close adviser of Empress Elizabeth, was attained could the university finally open.

The university began in a small, renovated wooden building that had formerly been a pharmacy. Mr. Lomonosov was forty-three years old when it opened.

THOUGH THE DOORS to Moscow State University eventually opened due to Mr. Lomonosov's tremendous efforts, at the time he was not widely recognized as the university's founder. He did not attend the opening ceremony or even teach at the university. Nevertheless, he remained in St. Petersburg and continued to dedicate his life to his lofty dream of fostering youth.

In one of his poems, he wrote:

> *Though my life may end*
> *in misfortune,*
> *if young minds blossom*
> *gloriously*
> *and follow the path I*
> *have pioneered,*
> *Russia will no doubt*
> *give birth*
> *to innumerable children*
> *to succeed me.*[6]

Moscow State University proved to be a new and innovative university for the Russian people as a whole. Not a single member of the nobility was in its first graduating class. Mr. Lomonosov's spirit that students should be respected not for their family origins but for their dedication to their studies was alive and well in the new school. Moreover, the classes were held not only in Latin, as was the tradition of the time, but also in Russian, because Mr. Lomonosov believed that if learning was to be made broadly available to the people, it had to be provided in their native language. The university was also innovative in allowing not just registered students but the general public to attend lectures and use its library.

A new age can only dawn when the people can acquire knowledge and develop wisdom.

The students who attended Moscow State University respected and admired Mr. Lomonosov. No doubt they felt that to carry on the spirit of the school's founder was to ensure its longevity.

The university's first major publication was a selection of Mr. Lomonosov's writings. The project was supervised by Nikolai Popovskii, a student of Mr. Lomonosov who later became a professor at the university. Unfortunately, Mr. Popovskii was struck down by illness and died before the book was finished. Mr. Lomonosov must have been deeply moved when he read the edition of his selected works that his late student had worked so hard to prepare.

Mr. Popovskii dedicated a poem to his teacher:

> *Lomonosov,*
> *a master of the rich Russian language,*
> *opened a palace of nature*

and demonstrated the
brilliance
of the Russian people
through education.[7]

The struggles of Mr. Lomonosov's students were a testimony to the truth and rightness of his efforts.

MOSCOW STATE UNIVERSITY had become a citadel of learning, contributing greatly to the development of the Soviet Union, and many of its graduates were recipients of the Nobel Prize or the Lenin Prize, the latter conferred by the Soviet government. Shin'ichi and his party sat at a round table in the rector's office with some twenty faculty representatives of the university, including Rector Khokhlov and Vice Rector Tropin, discussing various subjects.

Rector Khokhlov said eagerly: "Soka University seeks to educate capable young people for the sake of the twenty-first century, which is something that is an important concern of ours. In that regard, I believe there is great significance in promoting educational exchange between our two schools."

Shin'ichi was very moved by these words. Moscow State University was one of the leading institutions of higher learning in the Eastern Bloc. The rector, however, rather than simply resting on that authority, was sincerely thinking about what kind of people were needed for the next century. When leaders become authoritarian, there can be no fresh growth. Growth is another name for continuously thinking of the future.

The discussion covered a variety of topics concerning university education, such as: the selection of textbooks; correspondence course programs; the relationship between university departments and independent research institutes attached to the university; the state of graduate programs; hiring instructors and the qualifications they should have; and Japanese studies at Moscow State University. The Soka University president and a faculty member, who were traveling with Shin'ichi, had numerous questions about correspondence programs, as it had been decided to institute one at their school as well.

Moscow State University had some four thousand students in its correspondence program. Though the course of study was quite extended, when it was completed, graduates of the program received a regular university degree, and the correspondence program had a graduation rate of 90 percent.

After listening to the explanation of the Russian university's correspondence program, Shin'ichi said: "This program embodies your university's commitment to providing the best possible education to all citizens. In the twenty-first century, correspondence courses and other programs open to the public are certain to grow in popularity. I regard the twenty-first century as the century of education. I also believe we need to change the thinking that education exists for the sake of society and move toward a society that values and promotes education for all."

DURING HIS meeting with Moscow State University faculty members, Shin'ichi officially donated three thousand Japanese books to the school. Along with a catalogue of their titles, he presented Rector Khokhlov with twenty actual books that he had brought with him to the Soviet Union, including *Nihon kokogaku jiten* (Dictionary of Japanese Archaeology), *Nihon no bunka chiri* (Cultural Geography of Japan), *Nihon no bi to shizen* (Japanese Aesthetics and Nature) and *Gaisetsu Nihon bijutsu shi* (An Outline History of Japanese Art).

The three thousand books had been chosen with a focus on promoting an understanding of Japanese culture. In addition to books on Japanese history, culture, thought and art, there were a number of volumes related to education in Japan, as well as language books and dictionaries.

Shin'ichi regarded the donation of books as a way to build the foundation for cultural exchange. He had a strong memory of how reading translations of stories about foreign lands when he was a boy had provided him with a glimpse of life in other countries. Though the Japanese educational system at that time was under the control of the militarist government and thus subjected to many restrictions, books brought a fresh breeze from the outside world into Shin'ichi's life. That's why he now placed such importance on donating books as an initial step toward cultural exchange.

Rector Khokhlov accepted the catalogue of books and said with sincere appreciation: "We are very grateful. We will make the books you have donated available not only to students but to the general public."

High on the wall of the rector's office hung a large tapestry depicting the university's façade. "What a beautiful tapestry," Shin'ichi commented, upon which Rector

Khokhlov explained, "That was presented to us by Peking University to celebrate our two hundredth anniversary."

"I see!" Shin'ichi said. "It's from China!"

"That's right," the rector continued. "Though there may be tensions between our governments, the Soviet people have warm feelings for the Chinese people and think of them as their friends. That's why we still have this tapestry on display."

Shin'ichi was deeply moved. *This is it!* he thought. *Friendship and trust cultivated through educational exchange cannot be shaken by political tensions. This must be the way forward!*

A feeling of excitement rose in his heart. He looked up at the tapestry again, where the great citadel of education seemed to stand high above the rift between the Soviet and Chinese governments.

AFTER PRESENTING the books to Moscow State University, Shin'ichi and his party were given a tour of the university campus by Rector Khokhlov and other faculty members. Stepping out onto a balcony of the main building, they enjoyed a panoramic view of Moscow. Shin'ichi said to the rector, "Soka University is still a small, fledgling university, but it's my dream that in the twenty-first century it will be as well respected as your fine institution and make valuable contributions to the world."

Rector Khokhlov replied: "A university's significance is not measured by its size. Soka University has a wonderful founding spirit that champions universal human values. It has limitless potential. That's why we of Moscow State University wish to build a solid relationship with your school."

The members of Shin'ichi's party were once again taken aback by the rector's words. It simply hadn't occurred to them that the rector of a university in a socialist country could attach such importance to matters concerning the human spirit. But it was precisely because Moscow State University did so that it had such an illustrious record of achievement.

Mahatma Gandhi said to the effect that the power of the spirit is limitless and ever-advancing, and that nothing in the world could match the true potential of that power.[8]

Shin'ichi and his party next visited a geology classroom and a cultural facility where musical and theatrical performances took place. They also sat in on a mathematics lecture.

When they stepped outside, they came upon a statue of M. V. Lomonosov, the university's founder. Mr. Lomonosov was looking off into the distance with an expression of great fortitude and resolve. In the plaza where the statue stood, Shin'ichi engaged several students in conversation, asking them questions such as which foreign country they'd like to visit. Their responses were energetic and clear. When Shin'ichi asked which subject was the most difficult for them, one replied, "We chose this university and our majors because we had an area we wanted to specialize in, so even if some of our classes are difficult, they're interesting, and we challenge them earnestly."

"That's wonderful!" Shin'ichi said. "With that attitude, you will no doubt master even those subjects that don't come easily to you. A gifted student is none other than one who continues to study without cease."

SHIN'ICHI ASKED the students: "What's the biggest challenge as far as dormitory living is concerned?"

One of the students answered immediately, "Being on time for my morning classes!"

This humorous reply brought laughter from everyone gathered. Shin'ichi felt that the young people were being their natural selves with him. He envisioned them becoming friends with Soka University students and frankly sharing ideas and opinions. He was determined to usher in an age when this was possible and to foster youth so that they could make their way freely into the world.

The British philosopher Bertrand Russell wrote, "I think, nevertheless, that the most vital need of the near future will be the cultivation of a vivid sense of citizenship of the world."[9]

Shin'ichi smiled at the students and said: "I'm so happy to have had this opportunity to speak with you. I hope that in the future you'll come to visit the university I founded in Japan." As he shook their hands, he sensed the hope brimming in their hearts.

At three in the afternoon, after visiting Moscow State University, Shin'ichi and his party visited the headquarters of the Union of Soviet Societies for Friendship and Cultural Relations with Foreign Countries, an important Soviet organization focusing on nongovernmental exchange with foreign countries.

Chairperson of the union, Nina Popova, a recipient of the Lenin Peace Prize and a member of the Central Committee of the Soviet Communist Party and the Supreme Soviet of the U.S.S.R., welcomed the group. She was a large woman with a maternal air whose strong conviction shone in her eyes. Addressing Shin'ichi, she smiled and said in a booming voice: "Dialogue is a prerequisite for friendship. I'm very glad to have this opportunity to meet with you, President Yamamoto, the leader of one of the few truly international organizations in Japan, and to be able to exchange opinions with you."

She then turned to Shin'ichi's wife, Mineko, and the women's division representative in the group and remarked with passion: "As the poets have long said, it is women who most desire peace and try to preserve it. I believe that when individuals or nations are in a dangerous state of tension, women must take action out of their wish to prevent their grandchildren and great-grandchildren from ever becoming the victims of war."

AFTER TALKING for only a few minutes, Mrs. Popova and Shin'ichi found themselves in agreement on a fundamental point. That is, the importance of striving to create good, neighborly relations between Japan and the Soviet Union toward the ultimate aim of a world without war. Every word Mrs. Popova spoke was filled with a passionate commitment to peace. Her anger toward fascism was palpable as she said forcefully: "We must fight against fascism if we are to preserve culture. Unless fascism is eradicated, a country's culture is certain to perish." She was clearly speaking from her personal experience of history. During World War II, Nazi Germany had laid siege to the city of Moscow.

On the way from the airport to the hotel on the day of Shin'ichi's arrival (September 8), Moscow State University Vice Rector Vladimir Tropin had pointed out of the window of the car and said, "That is where we built our line of defense when the Nazis attacked Moscow." In October 1941, Nazi forces advanced on Moscow from the north, south and west, and a fierce battle to defend the capital began.

Shin'ichi understood Mrs. Popova's feelings only too well. "Yes, I agree," he said. "The eradication of fascism is one of the great challenges facing humanity. The first president of the Soka Gakkai fought against persecution by the fascist military authorities in Japan and died in prison. And our second president also stood up against the militarists and was imprisoned for his efforts.

Irs. Popova.
eko and the
group, "The
ou'll visit my
hildren." Her
s a mother and
of people that
to see.
we can just view
shared humanity,
the same ultimate
cial or political sys-
uman beings, there
rstand one another.
With his conviction
t the headquarters of
iendship and Cultural

s life and robbed me of
kai is an organization
ation and committed

s Shin'ichi spoke.
ecided to ask her
truth candidly is

pression of
is no free-

party visited was Mos-
he pillars of the historic
with its walls. After the
n in 1917, Lenin trans-
sburg to Moscow. It was
called on the Russian peo-
ainting of Lenin speaking
floor balcony hung in the

same
ices
n-
al

spoke
Isaev,
e city.

a Bu."
By th the
built

hin'ichi

and his party had formed a warm bond with N
As she showed them out, she said to Min
women's division leader traveling with the
next time you come to Moscow, I hope y
home and meet my children and grand
invitation brimmed with her compassion
as a human being. It was just this aspec
Shin'ichi had come to the Soviet Union

All people seek happiness and peace. I
one another from the standpoint of our
we will realize that we are all aiming fo
goal, regardless of how different our so
tems may be. Given that we are all h
is no reason why we shouldn't und
That is why dialogue is so important
in this truth deepened, Shin'ichi le
the Union of Soviet Societies for F
Relations with Foreign Countries.

The next place Shin'ichi and hi
cow City Hall on Gorky Street. T
structure contrasted beautifully
success of the Russian Revoluti
ferred the capital from St. Pete
from this very building that he
ple to build a new nation. A
in the snow from the second
city hall's corridor.

Here, Shin'ichi met and
mayor of Moscow, V. P.
Shin'ichi with the key to t

A S THE CITY official handed Shin'ichi the honor, he said: "We are hoping that you'll come and visit Moscow again. That's why we're presenting you with the key to the city."

They then sat down to talk. Mr. Isaev started by explaining city hall's connection to Lenin. He also described the time when they were forced to broaden the street passing in front of the building, saying: "The city hall wasn't demolished. Instead, the entire structure was moved 164 feet back. Also, since it was becoming somewhat cramped, a third story was added to the original two-story building. We regard the preservation of cultural treasures as one of the most important aspects of urban planning." His expression was proud as he uttered these remarks.

Mr. Isaev went on to speak in some detail of plans for the city's future, including solutions to Moscow's housing and traffic problems, as well as its strategies for garbage disposal, ensuring a safe and reliable water supply and combating environmental pollution. One such plan was to switch from using coal to natural gas in heating homes and buildings as a measure to alleviate air pollution. Implementing this, however, would require a substantial investment, as long pipelines would have to be built to carry natural gas from Siberia and other distant regions. The first deputy mayor was nevertheless determined to realize this goal, stating with conviction: "Nothing is more important than the health of our citizens. We will definitely make this happen."

Shin'ichi nodded in understanding. He was struck by the fact that all of the plans Mr. Isaev introduced gave top priority to the welfare of the people. Cities in Japan and around the globe also faced such problems as environmental pollution. It was therefore important for these cities to work together, transcending political and ideological differences, and pool the wisdom of humanity toward dealing with them. There are many ways in which cities worldwide can assist one another—for example, through the sharing of information and the exchange of planning ideas.

The Indian poet Rabindranath Tagore said, "It is the mission of civilization to bring unity among people and establish peace and harmony."[10]

Shin'ichi took such copious notes that his hand ached. He, too, was very concerned about the environment, regarding it as a pressing problem that humanity must solve.

AFTER VISITING Moscow City Hall, Shin'ichi and his party returned to their hotel, where reporters from TASS, the official Soviet government news agency, were waiting to interview him. Shin'ichi agreed readily to speak with them and candidly shared his impressions of the Soviet Union.

At seven that evening, he and the others attended a dinner held in their honor by Moscow State University at a restaurant in the city. It proved to be a wonderful opportunity to talk freely with university rector Rem Khokhlov and his wife, as well as other university representatives. The more Shin'ichi and Rector Khokhlov conversed, the more they opened up to each other. Rector Khokhlov was also quite determined to actualize an exchange program between Moscow State University and Soka University, and he said that he wished to explore concrete plans and make some decisions while Shin'ichi and the others were in the Soviet Union.

After dinner, the Japanese group went to see a view of the city from the Lenin Hills (present-day Sparrow Hills). As they looked out over the night scenery, Mineko, said: "The city lights are beautiful. I wonder if that area of buildings over there is apartments."

"Yes, it looks like it," Shin'ichi replied. "Each one of those lights represents a person's life. I really think that the purpose of politics and economics should be to protect those individuals' happiness. Once the spirit of serving the people, of making human beings the top priority, is forgotten, any society, no matter what its social or political system, will lapse into impersonal bureaucratism, its organizations will become rigid, and it will become tainted by greed and self-interest. That is why I'm so intent on communicating the philosophy of human revolution and the spirit of Buddhist humanism."

Every day of the visit to the Soviet Union was packed with various activities and meetings, and those traveling with Shin'ichi were on edge most of the time. By the end of the second day, they were exhausted. Speaking with his fellow travelers, Shin'ichi said: "Please try to enjoy yourselves. There's no need to be stressed or anxious. If you just be cheerful and positive, you'll shine as true diplomats."

On the following day, September 10, they were scheduled to visit the Ministry of Higher and Secondary Specialized Education, among other places. They gathered together with Shin'ichi in the lobby that morning and, after confirming that everyone was there, set out for the day. Having been encouraged by Shin'ichi the night before to relax and enjoy themselves, they did just that. They looked like elementary school students on a field trip. They made such an impression that their drivers also began to relax and have a good time.

VYACHESLAV YELYUTIN, the minister of higher and secondary specialized education, welcomed Shin'ichi and his party warmly at the entrance to his office. As if he had been waiting for this opportunity to talk with Shin'ichi, he began to speak passionately about his views on education, saying: "Education is the foundation of culture in every nation. As such, I think you can see a nation's future by looking at the education it provides."

"I agree completely," Shin'ichi replied.

Their conversation flowed smoothly from the start. Shin'ichi and the others asked various questions, and the minister responded. They discussed a number of subjects, including planned human resources development to meet the needs of society, education based on a global outlook and the relationship between specialized training and a general, well-rounded education. Shin'ichi was earnest, and the minister answered each of his questions wholeheartedly, commenting favorably on the quality of Shin'ichi's queries.

When Shin'ichi asked him to share his thoughts about how education should respond to the advance of science and technology, the minister replied: "Due to the tremendous rate at which science and technology are advancing, the information being taught to students is already outdated by the time they begin studying it. I therefore think we need to help students develop critical thinking, so that they are able to glean what information is vital from what they've learned and know how to evaluate and analyze it. This will be an important subject for education from now on."

He went on to say that in order to make the best use of new and specialized knowledge, people need to have well-rounded learning and sound character. Education that enables people to develop such character is becoming more and more necessary, the minister added.

Shin'ichi expressed his strong agreement with this view. The essence of education is indeed character formation.

The minister also emphasized the need, as science and technology advance, for qualified specialists in their fields to further their studies in order to acquire new technological expertise. "For example," he said, "if physicians learn how to use laser technology, they will be able to treat their patients with more modern methods. How to conduct such continuing education is a topic of great focus for us and we are doing our utmost to promote it. There is no end to education."

Continuous reform and progress in education is the key to a society's growth.

MINISTER OF Higher and Secondary Specialized Education Yelyutin had great hopes for the contribution that exchange between Moscow State University and Soka University would make to the development of education. Learning that the minister had graduated from the Moscow Steel Institute, Shin'ichi asked what had prompted him to pursue studies in the field of engineering.

Mr. Yelyutin said nostalgically: "I was basically influenced by Lenin. At a time when many aspects of our country, including industry and agriculture, were in a state of near collapse after the civil war, Lenin, with his keen insight, sent the message to young people that the most important thing was to acquire learning." Inspired by Lenin's call, the young Yelyutin had resolved to get a university education. Believing that engineering was the best way to help rebuild his country, he had entered the Moscow Steel Institute.

The Russian writer Maksim Gorky wrote in a letter to some young people, "Learning is the strongest force in the world."[11]

Shin'ichi was impressed that Lenin had realized the importance of educating the youth in order to rebuild the war-torn nation. Education creates the future. Shin'ichi had also devoted his energies to education because he regarded it as the driving force for constructing a new age.

At noon, following his meeting with Mr. Yelyutin, Shin'ichi and his party paid a courtesy visit to the Supreme Soviet in the Kremlin. The Kremlin was synonymous with the Soviet government because various government bodies of the Soviet Union were located there, but the original meaning of "kremlin" is fortress. Situated on the banks of the Moscow River, the Kremlin was surrounded by high red brick walls, inside which numerous towers rose into the sky.

At the Kremlin, Shin'ichi met with V. P. Ruben, chairperson of the Council of Nationalities, one of the two chambers of the Supreme Soviet. After cordially thanking the chairperson for the invitation to visit the Soviet Union, Shin'ichi said: "There is a saying 'A picture is worth a thousand words.' During my visit, I have learned how your people are striving to ease tensions around the world and I've confirmed the Soviet Union's strong commitment to peace."

SHIN'ICHI CONTINUED, "As people who are opposed to war and committed to the peace and happiness of all humanity, we of the Soka Gakkai pledge to sincerely continue pursuing friendly exchange with the Soviet Union, using this visit as a first step."

Knowing that this meeting with Mr. Ruben would be short, Shin'ichi wished to make sure it didn't end in a simple exchange of pleasantries. Rather, he hoped that it would serve as an opportunity, however brief, to open the way to peace and friendship. That is why he began by speaking of the Soka Gakkai's commitment to peace.

In response, Mr. Ruben said: "I have heard that you are a great scholar and humanist. We wholeheartedly welcome your visit." He then went on to describe the Soviet Union's fundamental policy toward realizing peace: "The Soviet Union wishes to have friendly relations with all nations. We seek enduring friendship. In order to actualize this goal, I believe it is necessary to start from what can be achieved and quickly move toward promoting mutual exchange. In that context, exchange between Moscow State University and Soka University will be very significant.

"The future belongs to the younger generation. Youth is in itself the hope of the future. When the youth of the world are linked by a new humanism, there will be world peace."

Nodding in agreement, Shin'ichi remarked: "I agree completely. In order to create a great river of friendship, it's important not to allow short-term interests to get in the way, but to earnestly foster friendship over a longer period of five to ten years. Toward that end, cultural exchange on the private level is crucial. I'm determined to devote my life to working to forge a path for non-governmental exchange between Japan and the Soviet Union."

Mr. Ruben smiled and shook Shin'ichi's hand firmly. "I have the deepest admiration for your commitment to peace," he said. The chairperson also had his sights set on the future.

The shared convictions of the two men resonated within the Kremlin walls.

AFTER HIS MEETING with Chairperson Ruben of the Council of Nationalities, Shin'ichi and his party were shown Lenin's office and living quarters in the Kremlin.

Vladimir Lenin founded the Bolshevik Party—fore-runner of the Soviet Communist Party—and led the Bol-shevik Revolution of October 1917, the second and last major phase of the Russian Revolution. He was largely responsible for the establishment of the world's first socialist state, the Soviet Union. And after the revolu-tion's success, for a period of four years and nine months starting in March 1918, he led the new Soviet state from his office in the Kremlin.

All of the rooms that Lenin occupied were very plain and modest. The writing implements he used were set out on his office desk, and the walls were decorated with a large map and other pictures. The dining room where he and his family ate was quite small, with just a rough table and four chairs situated between the sink and the cupboards. It was actually more of a kitchen than a dining room. The cupboards appeared to have been refashioned from bookshelves. The plates and bowls were a hodge-podge of sizes and patterns, and there was nothing luxurious or expensive to be seen. In addition, Lenin had given his sister the largest of the rooms allotted to his family. His own room had only a narrow iron bed and a desk and was very basic. This was how the Soviet Union's top leader lived in the Kremlin.

Shin'ichi felt as if he had glimpsed an important side of Lenin, who was keenly aware of the sufferings of the Russian people, and who had devoted his life to the revolution. It wasn't simply Lenin's great ideas or his dynamic activism that drew the people to him. His strong self-discipline and his rigorous moral integrity, clearly evident in his modest way of living—such a contrast to that of the czar and the Russian aristocracy—was no doubt also a factor. People's homes tend to reflect their lifestyles.

When individuals lose sight of lofty ideals and principles, it becomes manifest in the way they live their lives. If leaders of the people succumb to personal vanity, grow accustomed to extravagance, and seek only to secure a life of ostentatious luxury for themselves, then they have lost their original commitment to work for the happiness of the people and make society a better place. They are on a path of spiritual decline. Such individuals are no longer qualified to lead the people.

Before leaving Lenin's quarters, Shin'ichi wrote in the guest book there: "I will never forget the spirit residing deep in the hearts of the people. Shin'ichi Yamamoto."

SHIN'ICHI AND HIS party next visited the Grand Kremlin Palace (formerly the czars' Moscow residence). In sharp contrast to Lenin's simple living quarters, it was the height of luxury, adorned with sparkling chandeliers and gorgeous furnishings from the days of the czars—all of which had been supported by the labor of oppressed serfs under the feudal system. Revolution is a historical inevitability when the powerful oppress and exploit the people mercilessly. Shin'ichi was reminded of a passage from the novel *The Eternal City* by the British author Hall Caine that he had studied with his mentor, Josei Toda: "The people are the true sovereign, and the only rebels are the classes who oppress them."[12]

Buddhism, which expounds that all people possess the Buddha nature within, is also a teaching of the sovereignty of the people. And the Soka Gakkai's movement for kosen-rufu is aimed at actualizing a world in which the people are the true sovereigns and can lead happy and fulfilled lives.

After Shin'ichi and the others left the Kremlin, they went to the Tomb of the Unknown Soldier, located along the outer north wall of the Kremlin complex. They wanted to offer flowers as a symbol of their pledge to realize peace.

The Tomb of the Unknown Soldier was built to commemorate those who died in World War II. It consisted of a flat, horizontal, red granite slab some thirteen to sixteen feet in length, upon which rested a bronzed soldier's helmet. The Eternal Flame of Glory burned in front of it, symbolizing a prayer for peace. An elderly couple stood at the tomb, weeping quietly. Perhaps their son had died in the war. Here was a clear example of the tragic effects of war, equally heartbreaking for people around the world.

Shin'ichi and his party walked solemnly up to the tomb and laid the wreath they were carrying. They then chanted Nam-myoho-renge-kyo three times for the eternal happiness of those who had lost their lives in the conflict. On the white ribbons that adorned the floral wreath was written, in gold Russian lettering, "With a prayer for world peace."

When the day's activities were over, the group returned to their hotel. The hotel staff member who kept the keys for the rooms on their floor, a large middle-aged woman, said to Shin'ichi with a smile: "You visited the Supreme Soviet in the Kremlin today, didn't you? It was broadcast on the news earlier."

THE INTERPRETER conveyed the hotel staff member's words to Shin'ichi, who smiled and replied: "Yes, we did. And after visiting the Kremlin, we placed flowers on the Tomb of the Unknown Soldier."

The woman nodded in understanding. When Shin'ichi and his party first arrived at the hotel, she and the other women who looked after the room keys didn't smile at them, just treating them in a businesslike manner. Perhaps they were nervous dealing with guests from a nation affiliated with the West.

Each day, when Shin'ichi and Mineko dropped off and picked up their room key, they greeted the women warmly and tried to converse with them. The first step in diplomacy is having good relations with those in our immediate environment. As the days passed, the women began to open up and speak to Shin'ichi and Mineko in a friendly way.

Shin'ichi added: "I saw an elderly couple weeping in front of the Tomb of the Unknown Soldier. It was very sad. I am firmly opposed to war and will do everything I can to prevent it from ever happening again."

The woman lowered her eyes and murmured softly, "My husband also died in the war." Then, as if entrusting him with her heartfelt wish, she said to Shin'ichi, "Please create a world without war."

The people of the Soviet Union also suffered terribly during World War II and were earnestly seeking peace. And in their country as well, the greatest victims of the war were women and children.

Shin'ichi took the woman's words deeply to heart and said: "I'll do my best for peace! I hope you'll also work for peace. Your voice will help change the world."

The Indian poet Rabindranath Tagore said, "Women have the vital power more strongly in them than men have."[13] Women do indeed have the power to change history.

That night, Ivan Kovalenko, vice president of the Soviet-Japan Society and the person in charge of matters related to Japan in the International Department of the Central Committee of the Communist Party of the Soviet Union, came to visit Shin'ichi in his hotel room. In fluent Japanese, he said, "I'm sorry to interrupt your rest, but I wanted to speak with you."

His words were polite and his gaze intense. He shook Shin'ichi's hand vigorously.

MR. KOVALENKO had effectively been the one responsible for Shin'ichi's invitation to the Soviet Union. He was therefore extremely interested in the impressions of Shin'ichi and his traveling companions.

Shin'ichi said: "Thanks to you and all our hosts, our trip has been very meaningful so far. We deeply appreciate your efforts."

Mr. Kovalenko smiled broadly. The two men then sat down at the table in Shin'ichi's room and began to talk. It seemed that Mr. Kovalenko wanted to share his thoughts directly with Shin'ichi, and he came right out and said,

"I'm hoping that you will build a bridge of friendship linking the Soviet Union and Japan."

He went on to harshly criticize the actions of Japanese political leaders with regard to the drawn-out dispute between the two countries over the sovereignty of several small islands located to the northeast of the Japanese archipelago.

Addressing the joint communiqué issued by Japan and China in September 1972, concerning the intent of those nations to restore diplomatic relations, he said that in the interest of Soviet–Japan friendship, Japan should not conclude the peace and friendship agreement, which he felt was antagonistic toward the Soviet Union. The communiqué stated that neither Japan nor China would attempt to establish hegemony in the Asia–Pacific region, and that they opposed efforts by any other country or group of countries to do so.

According to Mr. Kovalenko, the reference to "any other country" implied the Soviet Union and thus represented a hostile stance. As such, it didn't belong in the Japan-China friendship treaty, he asserted, telling Shin'ichi that as the founder of the Clean Government Party, he should instruct the party to make efforts to remove that clause.

Shin'ichi felt that Mr. Kovalenko's perspective was completely mistaken, and he replied unhesitatingly: "I think you misunderstand. I founded the Clean Government Party, but I'm not a politician. I'm a religious leader and an educator. The Clean Government Party is an independent political party and acts based on its own policies and platform. I, therefore, never give them any instructions as far as political matters are concerned, and in fact, I am not allowed to do so. That's an ironclad rule." It's important to have the courage to say what needs to be said.

In a loud voice, Mr. Kovalenko declared, "No, if your claim of wishing to build friendship between the Soviet Union and Japan is not a lie, this is something you absolutely must do!"

POUNDING THE table emphatically, Soviet-Japan Society Vice President Ivan Kovalenko said to Shin'ichi with a stern gaze, "The Soka Gakkai mustn't make an enemy of the Soviet Union by supporting a treaty that is antagonistic toward this country!" His voice conveyed an adamancy that would brook no opposition.

Shin'ichi smiled and said, "Doesn't your hand hurt?"

Mr. Kovalenko looked at Shin'ichi as if the wind had been taken out of his sails.

Shin'ichi then said in a gentle manner: "Mr. Kovalenko, I didn't come to your country to engage in political negotiations. I accepted the invitation to visit the Soviet Union as a private individual and as an educator. I wish to help open the way for educational, cultural and nongovernmental, private exchange between our countries and to contribute to establishing a great momentum toward lasting peace and friendship."

Thumping on the table himself, Shin'ichi looked pointedly into Mr. Kovalenko's eyes as he added: "This inflexible and domineering attitude will only make people dislike the Soviet Union. People will think it's a country that cannot engage in dialogue. And that will only be to your disadvantage."

With a smile, Shin'ichi then said: "Is it really necessary

for the Soviet Union to worry about the kind of treaty that Japan and China negotiate between themselves? All the Soviet Union needs to do is conclude its own bilateral treaty with Japan—one that forms an even stronger and closer relationship than that between Japan and China. If the Soviet Union acts with broad-mindedness, it will win the trust of people around the world."

Their conversation continued at a lively pace.

In closing, Shin'ichi said: "It is my hope that our countries will forge ties of true friendship. Toward that end, I feel it is important for me to say what I think, frankly and openly. Let's continue to engage in dialogue and exchange our opinions freely."

After that evening, Mr. Kovalenko visited Shin'ichi's hotel room several times, and they had numerous candid conversations. Sometimes they argued, pounding their fists on the table like that first night. In the process, they became good friends.

It is when we courageously speak the truth that we are able to open the door to others' hearts and allow the light of the spirit to shine through. That is how the seeds of trust are cultivated. It is the true spirit of sharing Nichiren Buddhism.

SHIN'ICHI SPENT September 11, the fourth day of his visit to the Soviet Union, engaging in exchange in the educational and academic spheres. Shortly after ten in the morning, he and his party visited Moscow Elementary and Secondary School No. 682, where they observed classes in session and were shown various school facilities, including geography and biology classrooms. At half past eleven, they went to the Academy of Sciences of the Soviet Union, where Vice President Aleksandr Vinogradov welcomed them warmly.

"The academy will celebrate its two hundred fiftieth anniversary this year," Mr. Vinogradov said. "We are very happy to have you as visitors at this felicitous time."

Maksim Kim, a member of the academy who, when visiting Soka University in December of the previous year (1973), had informed Shin'ichi of the academy's wish to invite him to the Soviet Union, was also on hand to welcome the Japanese delegation.

Everyone sat around a table and had a friendly discussion. Here, too, Shin'ichi clearly shared his thoughts, saying: "I have always believed that when it comes to science, and particularly the natural sciences, the ideological divisions of East or West, socialism or capitalism, are meaningless. It is therefore possible, in my opinion, for scientists to overcome all such 'isms' and work together for the genuine progress of humanity and world peace."

Shin'ichi felt it was incredibly foolish to allow differing social systems or ideologies to divide people and become the cause for conflict and hatred. In fact, the reality of this situation in the world angered him deeply. That is why he strove to point the way to realizing human harmony.

The Russian writer Leo Tolstoy declared that the sole means of uniting people is their union in the truth.[14]

Mr. Vinogradov replied in a powerful, measured voice, "In the end, when science is based on truth, it walks the same road across all ideological barriers."

He looked at Shin'ichi intently, and Shin'ichi nodded in agreement.

Mr. Vinogradov then said with a smile, "It seems that I have passed your test."

Everyone laughed, and Shin'ichi sensed a warm humanity in the vice president's friendly countenance.

FOR SHIN'ICHI, the most important theme of his conversations with each person he met in the Soviet Union was finding a way to achieve human harmony. Shin'ichi proposed to Mr. Vinogradov that, in order to bring together academics and scientists from across the ideological boundaries of East and West, they initiate scholarly exchange between the Institute of Oriental Philosophy in Tokyo that Shin'ichi had founded and the Academy-affiliated Institute of Oriental Studies. As a preliminary step, they agreed on an exchange of academic publications.

They also discussed the issue of the destruction of the earth's environment and ecology. Mr. Vinogradov suggested that one of the fundamental reasons for the ongoing problem of ecological destruction was that humanity and nature had fallen into a state of conflict. Shin'ichi then introduced the Buddhist teaching of the "oneness of life and its environment," or the inseparability of human beings and nature. He emphasized the importance of achieving a harmonious balance among all living things in the universe from the perspective of the interconnection and interrelation of all life.

Shin'ichi also spoke of the concern that advances in science and technology could result in the neglect of humankind's spiritual development. He stressed that the cultivation of the human spirit toward using science for the happiness of humanity was one of the most pressing issues of the coming century.

Though their time together was brief, the two men enjoyed a meaningful and profound exchange.

Afterward, one of the youth division representatives from Japan who had sat in on the meeting said to Shin'ichi: "Sensei, you're able to talk knowledgeably on any subject with leaders around the world. How did you acquire such broad and deep knowledge?"

Shin'ichi replied: "At 'Toda University.' Mr. Toda thoroughly instilled me with the basics of a wide variety of subjects. For example, in science, he had me study the entire series of *Shin kagaku taikei* (New Science Compendium) so hard that I practically memorized it. We also studied the theories of the universe put forth by Russian-born U.S. scientist George Gamow. Mr. Toda was very strict, but his sternness really paid off, as far as I'm concerned, and I'm profoundly grateful for it.

"Most of all, Mr. Toda emphasized the study of Nichiren Buddhism. He thoroughly taught me to apprehend all phenomena and fields of learning from the perspective of Buddhism. By making the knowledge I gained a part of my thought and philosophy, it became true learning that was deeply ingrained in my life. The reason why internationally respected leaders in various fields pay attention to what I say is that my words are all firmly grounded in Buddhism."

SHIN'ICHI AND HIS party went from the Academy of Sciences of the Soviet Union to Moscow State University, where they were to attend a luncheon hosted by Rector Rem Khokhlov at two in the afternoon. When they arrived at the university, they were led into a reception room. Rector Khokhlov, Moscow State University Party Committee Secretary V. A. Protopopov, Vice Rector Vladimir Tropin and other department heads and faculty members were waiting for them. They were also joined by Higher and Secondary Specialized Education Vice Minister N. S. Yegorov, Union of Soviet Societies for Friendship and Cultural Relations with Foreign Countries Vice Chairperson A. M. Ledovskii and others whom Shin'ichi had met and become friends with during his visit.

Mr. Khokhlov made the opening greetings. Expressing a deep appreciation for Shin'ichi's humanity, he raised his glass and said, "A toast to the humanism promoted by President Yamamoto!" During the luncheon, many of the guests rose to speak or deliver toasts. Mr. Protopopov called strongly for working together to build a world free of war. Mr. Yegorov declared that education was the area that could make the greatest contribution to the development of Soviet–Japan relations, and proposed a toast to future exchange between Moscow State University and Soka University.

Eventually, Shin'ichi stood up to say a few words. Stating that educational and cultural exchange was the way toward building enduring friendship, he extended an invitation to Mr. Khokhlov and his wife to visit Soka University. He also introduced the profound wish of his mentor, second Soka Gakkai president Josei Toda, to eliminate all misery and suffering from the world, adding that as Mr. Toda's disciple, he was determined to do everything he could in his capacity as a private citizen to realize his mentor's dream of world peace.

The achievement of world peace is indeed the shared desire of mentor and disciple in the Soka Gakkai; it is the very spirit of kosen-rufu.

Next, the Soka University president announced the basic outline for exchange with Moscow State University, which had been agreed upon through discussions between representatives of the two schools during the Japanese delegation's visit: 1) exchange of faculty members; 2) exchange of academic and research materials; and 3) exchange of students and scholarly research teams.

Both parties were to work out concrete ways to begin to implement this vision while Shin'ichi and the others were still in the Soviet Union. The way for exchange between the universities had been opened.

A T THE END of the luncheon, Rector Khokhlov presented Shin'ichi with a bronze bust of Moscow State University founder Mikhail Lomonosov and other gifts, to commemorate the initiation of exchange with Soka University. The bust was quite heavy, which Shin'ichi interpreted as a symbol of the weight of the sincerity and friendship being proffered by Moscow State University.

Later that day, Shin'ichi was interviewed by Radio Moscow at his hotel. He then had a meeting with Maksim Kim of the Soviet Academy of Sciences. Because Mr. Kim hadn't been able to speak personally with Shin'ichi during his visit to the Academy, he came to see Shin'ichi at his hotel, bringing a scientist friend along.

Shin'ichi welcomed them both warmly. It was, in fact, his meeting with Mr. Kim in December of the previous year (1973) that had led to this visit, which was opening the path to friendship with the Soviet Union.

Shin'ichi presented Mr. Kim with one of his books, on the flyleaf of which he wrote: "Our meeting in this lifetime is something I'll never forget as long as I live.... You are an individual who has persevered in the pursuit of truth while giving his all for the revolution. I will continue to watch your efforts."

Mr. Kim was of Asian descent, and though Shin'ichi didn't know what his life had been like, it was clear that he was concerned about Asia, which was the scene of ongoing conflict and strife.

Mr. Kim said: "I have seen tragedy in my life, but I always regarded it as a trial for me to overcome. Though our backgrounds might be different, I know that the ultimate goal we both seek is happiness for all humanity."

Saying that the most important thing in life is to continue challenging our struggles with courage while heading in the direction of hope, Shin'ichi then remarked: "In this limited lifetime of ours, we should strive to work together for the happiness and peace of humankind. That's our mission as people who live in such a turbulent age."

As they parted, Mr. Kim said to Shin'ichi with deep feeling, "I am sincerely grateful that you, a true star of wisdom, were born in our beloved Asia, which has undergone so many years of conflict."

The two men felt a deep resonance with each other.

The true meaning of dialogue is to stir just such reverberations of the common desire for the happiness and peace of all people.

Shin'ichi next went to the Japanese embassy in Moscow to attend a reception that he had been invited to by the Japanese ambassador.

ON THE FOLLOWING day, September 12, Shin'ichi visited the Soviet Ministry of Culture, where he met with First Deputy Minister of Culture V. F. Kukharskii and Vice Minister of Culture V. I. Popov shortly after eleven that morning. During the meeting, Shin'ichi said that he hoped to promote cultural exchange with the Soviet Union through the Min-On Concert Association and the Fuji Art Museum. He wanted to build a bridge of art linking the two nations. Both Japanese cultural institutions had been eager to engage in exchange and had conveyed that wish to Shin'ichi prior to his visit to the Soviet Union.

Knowing that the Min-On Concert Association had successfully sponsored a tour of the Soviet National Academy Novosibirsk Ballet to Japan in the past (1966), Mr. Popov gladly consented to Shin'ichi's proposal. They agreed that they would send various folk music and dance troupes as well as amateur troupes to perform in each other's countries through the sponsorship of Min-On. Regarding the Fuji Art Museum, the suggestion was made that a variety of Soviet museums might cooperate in putting together a large art exhibition that could be shown in Japan. Toward that end, it was agreed that the Soviet Ministry of Culture, Min-On and the Fuji Art Museum would continue engaging in concrete, official negotiations.

The Japanese delegation next visited the Ministry of Education, where they met with First Deputy Minister of Education Fedor Panachin. Here it was decided to initiate an exchange of textbooks in order to increase understanding between Japan and the Soviet Union.

Shin'ichi was striving patiently, step by step, to forge a path of exchange. Though his efforts may have been modest, he was confident that each one was like a single thread being woven into a magnificent tapestry of humanistic exchange.

Nichiren Daishonin states, "Little streams come together to form the great ocean" (WND-I, 579). Great things are accomplished through the accumulation of the actions we take day after day. Shin'ichi was utterly committed to opening the way for peace and friendship with sincerity and quiet perseverance.

Just after four in the afternoon, Shin'ichi and his party went to the Moscow Young Pioneers Palace. The Young Pioneers was an organization dedicated to fostering boys and girls to be members of the Komsomol—the Communist Union of Youth, which was the youth wing of the Communist Party. During his visit to China (in May and June of that year, 1974), Shin'ichi had visited elementary and junior high schools as well as the Shanghai Children's Palace, where children engaged in afterschool activities. Knowing that interaction with children is the key to creating a path of friendship into the future, he also wished to visit the Young Pioneers Palace while in the Soviet Union.

THE YOUNG PIONEERS Palace was brimming with the energy and enthusiasm of children whose future lay before them. Shin'ichi and his party were given a tour of the facility by its director and six Young Pioneers. They saw children engaging in various activities, including ballet, music, sports and crafts. Wherever they went, they were greeted warmly.

The visitors were also treated to a demonstration by a group of children practicing gymnastics. And the dignified movements of the ballet dancers, who were rehearsing with intense concentration, moved them deeply. In

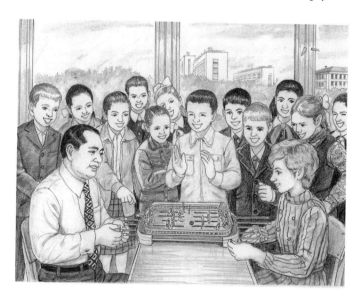

another room, Shin'ichi and some of the children played a game, which he lost every time. In the crafts room, he was presented with a large doll about 19.5 inches tall wearing clothes knitted by the girls in the class.

"Is this for me?" he said in surprise. "Why, thank you! I'll take this home and share it with my friends in Japan. We'll put it on display in the Kansai Soka Girls Junior High School and Kansai Soka Girls High School. I know the students will be delighted. Does this doll have a name?"

"No," the girls replied in Russian.

"All right, then, let's name her. Since she was born in Moscow, how about calling her 'Little Miss Moscow'?" The girls all smiled brightly, their faces shining with a glow that was common to little girls the world over.

After the tour of the Young Pioneers Palace, Shin'ichi presented the facility with a tape recorder manufactured in Japan, pictures drawn by Japanese elementary and junior high school students, and traditional Japanese percussion instruments called *zenidaiko* that had been handmade by members of the Soka Gakkai's Fife and Drum Corps.

Mineko, who was watching the children's expressions, whispered to Shin'ichi, "They look so sweet, don't they?"

Shin'ichi imagined them freely enjoying various games and sports with Japanese children.

That's an image of a global family, he thought to himself. *That's how the human race really should be.* In his heart, he pledged to make such an age come into being.

It is the mission of adults to open the way for a bright future for children.

When asked to sign the guestbook, Shin'ichi wrote: "I pray for the wonderful growth of these emissaries of the coming twenty-first century, and that Japanese and Soviet children will one day become true brothers and sisters. With my sincerest wishes for the development of this Young Pioneers Palace."

SHIN'ICHI'S SCHEDULE on this day was also extremely busy. Rector Rem Khokhlov of Moscow State University had invited him to a ballet performance of "The Nutcracker" at the Bolshoi Theatre that evening. It was wonderful to see a performance of this classic in Russia, the home of the music's composer, Pyotr Tchaikovsky.

While Shin'ichi talked with Mr. Khokhlov afterward, the subject turned to the battle between the soldiers of the Nutcracker and those of the mice in the ballet, which led to the topic of war in general. Shin'ichi asked Mr. Khokhlov, "When the German forces invaded, did you think that Moscow would fall?"

With a smile, Mr. Khokhlov replied: "No, I didn't. Moscow was subjected to heavy bombing, and in fact, a bomb was dropped on the Bolshoi Theatre. But the residents were utterly determined to defend their city. They loved Moscow. No one believed that Moscow would be taken by the Germans."

The strong commitment of the residents to defend their beloved city banished any fear of the enemy or cowardice that might try to take root in their hearts. They burned with an invincible will to win in the end. As the Soviet author Leonid Leonov (1899–1994) observed, all victory begins with victory over oneself.[15]

Late that night, Shin'ichi and his party took an overnight express train called the Red Arrow from Moscow to Leningrad (present-day St. Petersburg). The train was divided into compartments, each with a small table and a thick red carpet. It was a very pleasant eight-and-a-half-hour trip. Moscow University Vice Rector Vladimir Tropin and Senior Lecturer Leon Strijak, who was serving as their interpreter, accompanied the group to Leningrad.

They awoke the next morning, September 13, to a sea of green outside the train window. A forest of birch trees swayed gently in the soft rain. Leningrad was the second largest city in the Soviet Union. Founded in 1703 by the Russian czar Peter the Great, it is one of the world's most beautiful cities.

WHEN LENINGRAD was founded, it was known by the German name St. Petersburg. It was designated the capital of Russia in 1712, and in 1714 was renamed Petrograd, giving it a fully Russian name. The Russian Revolution began there in 1917, and after Lenin's death, it was renamed Leningrad in his honor. Then, after the collapse of the Soviet Union in 1991, it was restored to its original name, St. Petersburg.

Shin'ichi and the others arrived at Moscow Station in Leningrad. Stations were named after the destination of the trains that departed from them, and those leaving from this station were headed for Moscow, so it was called Moscow Station. In similar fashion, the station at which the group boarded the Red Arrow express in Moscow was called Leningrad Station.

When they stepped off the train, one of the youth division representatives traveling with Shin'ichi said, "The names of stations here in the Soviet Union are really confusing!"

Smiling, Shin'ichi replied: "It's just confusing because you're using Japan as your standard of comparison. Every country and region has its own culture, traditions and lifestyles. It's very important to accept them as they are. In fact, this way of naming stations exists in other countries as well. If you think about it, it's very logical. If you go to the station named after your destination, you are certain to get where you want to go, after all."

The young man was impressed by Shin'ichi's flexible attitude that wasn't attached to the way things were done in Japan. *Japanese people are always talking about being international*, he thought to himself, *but actually we measure everything against the Japanese way of doing things. Such thinking, however, implies that we've already created a barrier in our hearts to being genuinely international. But President Yamamoto accepts those differences and respects them. This must be the most important attitude for building mutual understanding and friendship.*

At the station, Shin'ichi and his party were greeted by Leningrad State University Vice Rector L. I. Seznyakov, Soviet-Japan Society Leningrad Branch Head L. A. Chebadaryov and Director N. A. Urakov and other officials.

"Welcome!" they called out in Russian.

"Thank you for coming here to meet us," Shin'ichi said.

A new friendship was thus initiated. The fostering of that friendship was sure to lead to the creation of a solid network for peace.

WHEN SHIN'ICHI and the others left the station, they stepped out onto Nevsky Avenue, a major thoroughfare that appears in Dostoyevsky's novel *Crime and Punishment*. The avenue was loved by many other Russian writers as well, including Pushkin and Gogol. Many of the buildings along the street were five stories high, and their richly historical stone facades created a wonderful harmony with the water flowing along the nearby canal.

In the afternoon, Shin'ichi and his party toured the city. Standing in Decembrists Square, they could see Saint Isaac's Cathedral, the former Naval Ministry and other grand edifices. "Decembrists" referred to a group of reformist officers who initiated a revolt in December 1825 to put an end to serfdom and dictatorship. The square commemorates their uprising. It was here that the Bronze Horseman, known from Pushkin's narrative poem of the same name, stood. The group also visited the Smolny Institute, which had been a girls' school during the time of the czars and was the place from which Lenin later led the October Revolution. At three in the afternoon, they went to the Piskarevskoye Memorial Cemetery, where many of those killed during World War II were buried.

During the war, the German forces laid siege to Leningrad for some nine hundred days, but the city's residents and the Russian soldiers stationed in the city joined forces to launch a stalwart defense. More than a million Russian soldiers and civilians died, of which more than six hundred thousand succumbed to starvation. Nevertheless, they refused to allow their city to be taken. They united and fought to the end to protect their home.

When people of all walks of life pool their strengths, they can form a solid bastion that no enemy can topple. When the people rise into action, history changes.

In praise of the indomitable struggle of its people, Leningrad was awarded the title Hero City (in 1945).

It was raining when Shin'ichi and the others reached the cemetery. They viewed the museum at the cemetery's entrance, which included displays about the defense of Leningrad. One of the items on display was Hitler's order to wipe the city from the face of the Earth.

As they took in the exhibition, Leon Strijak, the group's interpreter, explained: "The fierce attack continued, food supplies had reached zero, and the people were facing starvation. They were surrounded by the German army, and there was no way to bring fresh supplies or fuel into the city. The people thus came up with a plan."

MR. STRIJAK'S voice grew more animated: "Lake Ladoga was located on the northern edge of the city. The citizens of Leningrad waited for the lake to freeze over and then began to bring supplies in over the ice as well as evacuate some of the residents. They put children and old people into trucks, while those who had the physical stamina walked across the ice. When the ice melted, they used boats. A million people escaped by this means. The pathway across the ice was known as 'The Road of Life.'"

Shin'ichi's attention turned to several pieces of discolored paper that were part of the display. A bouquet of red flowers was placed in front of them. Mr. Strijak explained: "These are notes written by a little girl named Tanya Savicheva, known as 'Tanya's Diary.' Her father died when she was five years old, and the other members of her family died of cold and hunger during the siege."

Mr. Strijak translated the yellowed pages: "'Zhenya died 28 December, 12:30 in the morning, 1941.' Zhenya was her older sister. 'Babushka [Grandmother] died 25 January, 3 o'clock [in the afternoon], 1942.' 'Leka died 17 March, 5 o'clock in the morning, 1942.' Leka was her older brother."

The next pages that Mr. Strijak translated were about the deaths of her uncles Vasya and Lesha.

Lastly, he read: "'Mama, 13 May, 7:30 [in the morning], 1942,' 'The Savichevas have died,' 'All died,' 'Only Tanya remains.'"[16]

The nine pieces of paper recorded the facts without emotion, but the little girl's pain and grief pierced the reader's heart like a knife, because the reality she described was so cruel. And Tanya followed her family soon after, her short life coming to an end when she was only twelve years old.

In *War and Peace*, Leo Tolstoy (1828–1910) describes war as follows: "An event took place counter to all the laws of human reason and nature."[17]

His entire body trembling in anger, Shin'ichi murmured to himself: "How awful. What an unspeakable tragedy. This must never be allowed to happen again!"

AS THEIR FRIENDS and neighbors died one by one, the residents of Leningrad helped one another withstand the hunger and cold, sharing the small amount of bread they had and huddling together for warmth. One of their sole sources of encouragement was the daily radio broadcasts. In response to an appeal from the radio station, writers went on the air to deliver lectures, poets to read their poems and famous singers to perform, expressing an undying pride in their city and imparting hope, courage and confidence of eventual victory to the city's residents.

At one point, the radio in most areas of the city fell silent because there was no power for transmission. Residents assembled at the station to implore that the station be put back on the air. One said that while they could withstand having their food rations cut, they couldn't bear to go without the broadcasts.

The artists were utterly committed to the radio shows. One poet insisted on reading his verses in spite of being in a terribly weakened state from starvation. He actually collapsed after he finished his broadcast and died a few days later. And a singer who was so frail that he had to support himself with a cane died the same night after his radio performance.[18] But these selfless voices were a tremendous source of courage and inspiration to the people, enabling them to endure the unendurable.

The brutal attack on the city continued, and a great many residents died. Nevertheless, on the nine hundredth day of the siege, Leningrad was still standing. They had won.

When the war finally ended, a spacious, green cemetery was built in memory of those who had fallen. It was the Piskarevskoye Memorial Cemetery. Shin'ichi and his party made their way from the museum at the entrance of the cemetery to lay flowers at the memorial in the cemetery proper, where some five hundred thousand people were buried. The rain lifted and the numerous trees planted on the grounds glistened in the sunlight. While a funeral march played from somewhere in the distance, the group walked toward a statue at the rear of the cemetery called Monument to the Motherland. It depicted a woman holding out a wreath made of oak sprigs, a symbol of the invincible spirit of the people of Leningrad.

To Shin'ichi, it seemed that the statue was calling out earnestly for peace while suppressing a profound grief at the loss of so many lives in the war. It was a large monument, about thirty-nine feet tall including the base. It was as if its massive size was conveying the enormity of the people's sorrow.

SHIN'ICHI AND THE others paid their sincere respects to the deceased as they laid flowers at the base of the monument, chanting Nam-myoho-renge-kyo solemnly three times and vowing to realize peace.

There were several tombstones in the cemetery that lacked individual names, simply inscribed with a year, such as "1942." These were mass graves of large groups of anonymous citizens and soldiers.

Behind the monument was a wall bearing an inscription. It was a poem by the Russian poet Olga Berggolts, who had been in charge of the radio broadcasts during the siege of Leningrad and had read poetry over the airwaves to encourage and inspire the people. Mr. Strijak translated the poem for Shin'ichi and his party:

> *Here lie Leningraders,*
> *Here are townsfolk, men, women, children.*
> *By their sides are*
> *Red Army soldiers.*
> *With their entire lives*
> *They defended you, Leningrad,*
> *The cradle of the Revolution.*
> *We cannot enumerate all their noble names here,*
> *So many are there under the eternal granite guard.*
> *But know, when honoring these stones*
> *Nobody is forgotten and*
> *nothing is forgotten.*[19]

Shin'ichi's heart filled with emotion. He nodded silently and chanted Nam-myoho-renge-kyo three times again.

When they returned to the car, Shin'ichi turned to Mr. Strijak and said with righteous anger in his voice: "I had no idea. In fact, most Japanese are unaware of just how terribly the Soviet people suffered during the war.

Why don't Soviet leaders try to communicate this truth more widely to the world? If they won't do it, I will, in whatever small way I can!" His words resounded with firm resolve.

Moscow State University Vice Rector Vladimir Tropin, who was riding in the same car, was taken aback by Shin'ichi's tone of voice. He asked the interpreter what Shin'ichi was so angry about, and if they had done something to upset him. When he heard Mr. Strijak's explanation, tears rose in his eyes. He was deeply moved by Shin'ichi's feelings for those who had died in the war and his hatred for war itself.

Without indignation at the great evil of war, humanism cannot exist. As the French philosopher Jean-Jacques Rousseau remarked, "Virtue ... is inflamed with indignation against crime."[20]

JUST AFTER five that afternoon, Shin'ichi and his party visited the Leningrad City Hall. A banner reading "Welcome" in Japanese hung on the landing above the stairway inside the building. Shin'ichi expressed his profound appreciation to the mayor of Leningrad, who proceeded to speak a little about the city's history as well as its present circumstances. His words conveyed a pride in Leningrad's role as a center of traditional culture and the Russian Revolution.

The mayor presented Shin'ichi with a medal of the city of Leningrad that was engraved with an image of Lenin on one side. He then gave Shin'ichi and the others a tour of the city hall. Shin'ichi was deeply touched by the mayor's obvious wish to promote friendly relations.

That evening, at the invitation of the Leningrad Branch of the Union of Soviet Societies for Friendship and Cultural Relations with Foreign Countries, Shin'ichi and his party went to see an ice ballet. Shin'ichi and Mineko enthusiastically applauded the dynamic and beautiful performance.

On the morning of the following day, September 14, the Japanese delegation visited Leningrad State University, the oldest university in the Soviet Union, which was celebrating its two hundred fiftieth anniversary. The institution had many fine alumni to be proud of, among them such eminent figures as the chemist Dmitri Mendeleyev, known as the primary creator of the periodic table of elements; physiologist Ivan Pavlov, renowned for his experiments with classical conditioning; and numerous other Nobel laureates. Shin'ichi and his party were greeted with warm smiles, as if they were old friends, by Vice Rector L. I. Seznyakov, economics department head N. A. Moiseenko and other faculty members.

When everyone was seated, Vice Rector Seznyakov said joyously: "The greatest pride of our university is its revolutionary spirit. The dedication to overcome any obstacle in order to acquire learning for the welfare of the people is alive in all the study and research conducted here."

Leningrad State University carried on holding lectures even during the German siege of the city, convening them in dugout bomb shelters. Even the dissertations of Ph.D. candidates continued to be assessed in underground shelters as well as in the basements of various facilities during the fighting. These assessments were handled with utmost seriousness, and no special leniency was shown because of the war going on. Many new doctors of philosophy were born amid the fierce onslaught of the German forces.

Shin'ichi said: "That's wonderful. The revolutionary spirit is a spirit of challenge. It is a powerful determination that rejects all complacency, laziness, cowardice or idleness. It is the force that creates a brighter future."

IN THEIR discussions, Shin'ichi and Leningrad State University Vice Rector L. I. Seznyakov, along with other faculty members, agreed on the importance of cultural exchange in deepening friendship between Japan and the Soviet Union. Leningrad State University was the first university in the Soviet Union to establish a Japanese department, having done so in the days before the Russian Revolution. Dr. Evgenia Pinus, a professor of Japanese language who was present during the talks, spoke in fluent Japanese of the university's Japanese-language program. She then said to Shin'ichi, "I am very eager to engage in exchange with Japan in order to help our students deepen their understanding of contemporary Japan."

"I think that's a great idea," Shin'ichi replied. "Let's make it happen. Let's build a beautiful bridge of culture linking our two countries."

Scholars and educators who are concerned about the future of humanity all share a desire for exchange between people that transcends national and ideological barriers. The world is one, and the human race is one. For people to reach out to one another and work together is a historical inevitability.

After speaking with the vice rector and faculty members for about an hour, Shin'ichi met with some student representatives. He asked about student life, the students' views on marriage, what they regarded as the goal of their studies and other topics. All of the students were focused on the twenty-first century. Their eyes sparkled with hope. The Russian author Nikolay Gogol (1809–52) wrote, "Youth is fortunate in the fact that always before it there lies a future."[21]

Shin'ichi and his party next visited Peter the Great's Summer Palace and the State Hermitage Museum. The Summer Palace, or Petrodvoretz, was located 18.6 miles southwest of the city center. Though it had originally been built for the czar, it was now a spacious place for ordinary citizens to relax and refresh themselves surrounded by greenery and fountains. The outdoor fountains were terraced and beautifully decorated with sculptures.

The Hermitage Museum was in the city center. Originally serving as the winter palace of many Russian czars, it was now a world-class museum. Shin'ichi was deeply impressed to see paintings by Rembrandt, Raphael and other such artists on display, and he thought how wonderful it would be if the Japanese people could view these treasures of humanity in their own country. He resolved to open the way to artistic exchange between Japan and the Soviet Union.

THE TIME WAS fast approaching when Shin'ichi and his party would have to say farewell to Leningrad, for they were scheduled to return to Moscow by overnight train that evening. At seven, the Leningrad

Branch of the Union of Soviet Societies for Friendship and Cultural Relations with Foreign Countries sponsored a banquet for the Japanese delegation at the hotel where they were staying. The vice branch head delivered opening remarks: "We are overjoyed to have had this opportunity to welcome President Yamamoto and his party to Leningrad. The people of both our countries strongly desire friendship and peace. In that sense, we are all of like mind. I would like to offer a toast to the great success of President Yamamoto's future endeavors and to friendship between our two countries."

Everyone raised their glasses in a toast. Amicable conversations began among those in attendance. Shin'ichi was struck by the thought: *Everyone I have met here in the Soviet Union longs for peace and wishes to form friendships that transcend national boundaries. Their hopes and dreams must be made a reality! That is part of my life's struggle.*

With profound gratitude to his hosts and a heartfelt commitment to broadly blazing a path to friendship between the two nations, Shin'ichi stood up and said: "The Soka Gakkai is an organization built through the initiative of ordinary Japanese people. This visit has opened the way to exchange between the peoples of Japan and the Soviet Union. I will continue to devote myself earnestly to the promotion of bilateral friendship as a way to ensure peace.

"During this visit, I learned of the powerful outrage against war felt by the people of Leningrad, of their deep and passionate wish for peace and of their broadmindedness and their openness to friends around the globe. This trip has been a significant experience for me. I sincerely pray that Leningrad, one of the world's leading centers of culture, will continue to grow and prosper as a capital of peace and progress, for the sake of the happiness of the people."

Those who have experienced the tragedy of war have a mission to speak out for peace. The Russian writer Leo Tolstoy said: "People are born into this world with a mission. Instead of putting it off, we should devote our every moment to achieving it. That's the only way to true happiness."[22]

The dinner ended at half past nine.

TRAVELING ONCE again on the Red Arrow overnight express train, Shin'ichi and his party arrived in Moscow the next day, September 15. The weather in Moscow was like early winter.

After checking into their hotel, they set out at about noon for the city of Zagorsk (present-day Sergiyev Posad), a religious center. Their Soviet hosts had strongly recommended this side trip. Led by a police escort, the ten or so cars headed for their destination. From the car windows, the Japanese visitors could see wide harvested fields and birch forests, their leaves turning a golden hue. They arrived in Zagorsk after about an hour. Located forty-three miles outside central Moscow, Zagorsk was a center of the Russian Orthodox Church dating back to the fourteenth century.

Shin'ichi and his party toured the historic Cathedral of the Assumption with its onion domes, as well as other religious buildings. The cathedral was filled with elderly women deep in prayer.

The urge to pray is profoundly ingrained in human nature. Without hope, people cannot survive, and as long as hope exists, prayer exists. The Russian writer Anton Chekhov (1860–1904) observed, "A [person] must have faith, or must search for a faith, or his life will be empty."[23]

The Japanese delegation next visited the Theological Academy in Zagorsk, where they had lunch with the Academy rector. "Soviet religious leaders warmly welcome all of you, as people who are working for world peace!" the rector said. Turning to Shin'ichi, he then spoke about the academy's activities. Shin'ichi responded by asking about various matters, including the state of religion in the Soviet Union.

In Zagorsk, the Russian Orthodox Church seemed to be deeply rooted in the lives of the people in the way of customs and traditions. It also apparently offered the people comfort and support. But it did not seem to be fulfilling the true role of religion as a source of spiritual power to inspire new creativity. Without people's spiritual growth, a society cannot truly shine with hope. It occurred to Shin'ichi that the Soviet Union faced a major challenge in finding a way to spiritually revitalize its people.

SHIN'ICHI ASKED the Theological Academy rector, "Why did you decide to study theology?" It was a personal question.

With a warm expression and carefully chosen words, the rector replied: "I think that each of us has a mission to fulfill. When all is said and done, I guess I followed my heart. I lost my elder brother in World War II, and it was a terrible shock to me."

It seemed that the death of his brother led the rector on

a quest for religion. Only religion can provide an answer to the problem of death. Tolstoy observed, "The essence of any faith consists in giving a meaning to life that will not perish with death."[24]

Shin'ichi nodded in understanding, saying: "I see. I also lost my eldest brother in World War II. My other three elder brothers all fought in the war, too. I myself was suffering from tuberculosis at the time. I am keenly aware of the terrible nature of war. When the war ended, I had serious doubts about State Shinto, which was used as a spiritual pillar to unite people in the war effort.

"Then, at the age of nineteen, I met Josei Toda, who later became the second president of the Soka Gakkai. Learning that the Soka Gakkai was one of the few organizations to resist the militarist authorities, I began to practice Nichiren Buddhism in search of a new philosophy of life."

The two men sensed that they had much in common. For both of them, the loss of their brother in the war and their desire for peace had triggered a seeking mind toward religion.

The rector next asked, "What do you think of religion-based peace movements?"

Shin'ichi replied: "The crucial question is whether such movements are really rooted in the people and have their support. I also think that peace activities should never be exploited as a way to promote any one religion. Moreover, such movements need to have a clear vision of the fundamental causes of war and be strongly grounded in reality." The rector nodded in agreement.

When their meeting came to an end, Shin'ichi was asked to sign the guest book. He wrote: "Extending and expanding a bridge of genuine humanity. Soka Gakkai President Shin'ichi Yamamoto."

Though their meeting was brief, they had enjoyed a meaningful religious dialogue.

THE FOLLOWING day, September 16, was the day for Moscow State University and Soka University to sign the academic exchange agreement that they had been negotiating since the start of Shin'ichi's visit to the Soviet Union. The signing of the agreement would make exchange between the two universities a concrete reality and set the wheels for it in motion.

When they left the hotel, Shin'ichi said to the Soka University president and the rest of his party: "Let's build Soka University into a world-class institution, a university that produces truly international individuals. I'll continue to make every effort to open the way to that goal."

Various Soviet media outlets, including television and newspapers, were waiting at Moscow State University to cover the signing ceremony. Arriving at the campus just before noon, Shin'ichi and his party were welcomed by Rector Rem Khokhlov and other university representatives. They all sat down at a round table.

As the television cameras rolled, Rector Khokhlov and the Soka University president signed Russian and Japanese versions of the exchange agreement between the two universities. The agreement began with a sort of preamble stating their common goals: "Soka University and M. V. Lomonosov Moscow State University, both seeking to make a contribution toward strengthening friendship and peace efforts between Japan and the Soviet Union, and believing that the expansion of academic exchange and cooperation is significant in deepening the mutual understanding of the Japanese and Soviet peoples, have agreed on the following points with the purpose of conducting academic exchange between the two institutions."

This was followed by six provisions, allowing for the exchange of professors and assistant professors, periodicals, scholarly resources and materials concerning university education, as well as plans for the exchange of doctoral students.

As Shin'ichi watched the signing ceremony, a vision of his beloved Soka University students passed through his mind. He was happy that, for the sake of the future, the way for academic and educational exchange with the Soviet Union had been opened. It was still a single, narrow path, but just as a stream eventually becomes a mighty river, he was certain that continued exchange

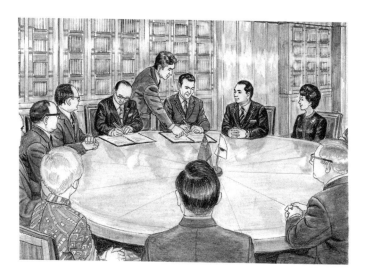

would eventually forge this small path into a broad and expansive road.

When the signing ceremony was over, Shin'ichi said to Mineko: "I'm imagining exchange between Moscow State University and Soka University thirty or fifty years from now. Someday, not just faculty members but students, hundreds of young people, will cross this bridge of exchange."

Mineko replied with a smile: "A new page of history has been written. A golden bridge to the future has been built."

AFTER THE EXCHANGE agreement was signed, Shin'ichi attended a luncheon sponsored by the Union of Soviet Societies for Friendship and Cultural Relations with Foreign Countries. Following that, he went to visit Nobel laureate Mikhail Sholokhov at his Moscow apartment. Shin'ichi was excited to meet the author. He had read many of his works, including *And Quiet Flows the Don*, a novel about Cossack farmers living in the area around the Don River at the height of the Russian Revolution.

Shin'ichi had requested a meeting with Mr. Sholokhov because he felt a strong sympathy with the theme of the author's writing—that history is made by ordinary people. But the author was in poor health and recovering at his hometown in the Rostov Region outside of Moscow, so it didn't look like the meeting would take place. Then, the morning of the previous day, Shin'ichi had received word that he would be able to see Mr. Sholokhov in Moscow.

The author's apartment was on the fourth floor of a

modest apartment building in central Moscow. Mr. Sholokhov had changed into a suit to meet Shin'ichi, whom he greeted cordially. Shin'ichi was deeply humbled to be treated with such consideration by a writer he respected so highly.

People of great character shine with sincerity. Human virtue is the embodiment of sincerity and integrity.

Shin'ichi's conversation with Mr. Sholokhov began at four in the afternoon. "I am honored to have this opportunity to meet you," Shin'ichi said as they shook hands. "This is one of the best days of my life."

The author smiled broadly and replied: "Welcome! I've been looking forward to this encounter."

Mr. Sholokhov would turn seventy the following May (1975). Shin'ichi had heard that the author's health was waning and that he had not attended a recent meeting of the Union of Soviet Writers. But seeing him in person, Shin'ichi noted that Mr. Sholokhov's color looked good and he appeared to be quite well.

Feeling somewhat relieved, Shin'ichi asked the author, as a representative of fans of Mr. Sholokhov's work around the globe: "How is your health? You are very important to many people in the world. Please take good care of yourself."

"Thank you," Mr. Sholokhov replied. "Health is important for everyone. Please take care of yours, too."

A T AROUND this time, Mikhail Sholokhov was facing a controversy over the accusation that *And Quiet Flows the Don* had been plagiarized. Just before Shin'ichi's trip to the Soviet Union, a Soviet writer living in exile abroad had put forth the claim that the novel was the

work of another writer, and that Mr. Sholokhov had sto-
len it. The West may have also fanned the controversy,
not wishing to accord the recognition represented by the
Nobel Prize to a Soviet author.

In spite of everything, Mr. Sholokhov seemed unshaken.
His eyes sparkled and he was brimming with vigor.

Many years later, Mr. Sholokhov's original drafts of
And Quiet Flows the Don were discovered, and computer
analysis also provided strong corroboration that it was
indeed his original work. The great Russian poet Pushkin declared, "All people of high reputation are inevitably
dogged by defamation, but when the truth is revealed,
lies will always be exposed as baseless."[25]

Mr. Sholokhov asked Shin'ichi, "Have you been to
Rostov?"

Rostov was a region located in southern Russia associated with the Cossacks. It was the place of Mr. Sholokhov's birth and also the setting for his masterpiece, *And
Quiet Flows the Don*. The writer's question reflected his
pride and love of his home.

To feel pride in and love for the place where one was
born is a source of happiness; it is the starting point of
personal pride and self-confidence.

Shin'ichi responded: "No, I wasn't able to visit Rostov
this time, but I would definitely like to go there with you
sometime in the future. Please remain in good health so
that we may do so. Eastern thought teaches that dedicating one's life to a profound mission brings health. Having
a sense of mission is of prime importance."

The author nodded in agreement. "I share that belief,"
he said. "I've been hospitalized on several occasions, but

I've overcome my illness. I've never forgotten my sense of personal mission."

Tolstoy wrote, "An enlightened person understands the meaning and purpose of his life."[26] These are wise words indeed.

A SENSE OF mission gives one strength, courage and energy. People shine their brightest when they are striving to accomplish their chosen mission in life. Mr. Sholokhov was living testimony of that fact.

With a playful smile, Mr. Sholokhov said: "Mr. Yamamoto, when I traveled to Japan many years ago, I followed Japanese customs. Now that you're in Russia, I believe you should follow Russian customs." As Shin'ichi was trying to figure out what the writer was implying, Mr. Sholokhov continued: "Let's raise our glasses. Let's drink together."

Shin'ichi was in a bind, since he couldn't drink alcohol. "I'm happy that you want us to drink together, but I'm afraid alcohol doesn't agree with me."

"No, it will be fine!" Mr. Sholokhov insisted. "Let's drink. If you really care about my health, you'll indulge me. Bring out the cognac! Tolya!"

"Tolya" was the nickname of Mr. Sholokhov's assistant, Anatoli, who looked after the writer.

In spite of Mr. Sholokhov's insistence, Anatoli made no motion to serve any alcohol. He was concerned about Mr. Sholokhov's health, and seemed to be trying to find a way out of the situation, but the author shouted: "We have an important guest today! We can make an exception!"

Finally, Anatoli brought out a bottle of cognac and two glasses. Smiling, Mr. Sholokhov whispered to Shin'ichi, "The doctor's coming to see me later, so let's drink up now." And with that he lifted his glass, toasted and drank it down in one gulp. Wishing to be polite, Shin'ichi also raised his glass and merely pressed it to his lips.

But Mr. Sholokhov told him to drain his glass. The interpreter Leon Strijak also urged Shin'ichi to drink, explaining that in Russia leaving alcohol in one's glass was regarded as very unlucky. Shin'ichi said, "I think that for our health it would be better if neither of us emptied our glass."

"I disagree," Mr. Sholokhov said. "This is a point on which we cannot see eye to eye." He laughed heartily and again urged Shin'ichi to drink. Shin'ichi finally gave in and drank the glass of cognac—upon which his host immediately filled it again! Shin'ichi knew that if he drank another glass he would pass out. It was an unexpected situation, and the others traveling with him watched with anxiety.

AS MR. SHOLOKHOV encouraged him to drink his second glass of cognac, Shin'ichi raised it, touched his lips to the rim and then passed it behind his back. One of those traveling with him, realizing Shin'ichi's predicament, took the glass from his hand and drank it for him. Mr. Sholokhov couldn't help but smile at Shin'ichi's humorous response and his companion's quick thinking. The members of Shin'ichi's party continued to take turns drinking for Shin'ichi, and soon their faces grew bright red.

Shin'ichi said: "I cannot drink, but my mentor, the

former president of the Soka Gakkai, could hold his alcohol. The president before him, however, couldn't drink either. So we seem to have a tradition of alternating between presidents who can and cannot drink."

From there, the conversation easily moved on to the past presidents and early history of the Soka Gakkai. To Shin'ichi, for whom the mentor–disciple relationship was the foundation of his spirit, thought and life, this was an extremely natural progression. He went on to explain how the first two Soka Gakkai presidents had stood up against persecution at the hands of Japan's militarist authorities.

Shin'ichi then said with a smile, "Today, I'd like to ask you to convey a message to all the fans of your writing around the world."

The author replied happily, "My only wish is that all of them will lead wonderful lives and be even happier than I am." He then added: "Incidentally, I recall that I received a very warm reception when I went to Japan. That trip is still one of my fondest memories. Please give my very best to all my friends in Japan."

Shin'ichi next asked Mr. Sholokhov for a message to the youth of the twenty-first century. The author replied: "I'm an optimist, so I believe that life in the twenty-first century will be, as young people hope, much better than it is today. At the same time, I sincerely pray that it will be so."

Mr. Sholokhov's youth had been spent in the time of civil war that followed the Russian Revolution. A supporter of the revolution, he had been taken prisoner by the opposing forces and condemned to death by firing squad. Having survived those trials, he subscribed to an optimistic philosophy and had faith in the future.

Optimism based on firm convictions is the source of hope and inner strength.

SHIN'ICHI NEXT asked Mr. Sholokhov what he thought was the key to friendly relations between Japan and the Soviet Union. Carefully choosing his words, the author replied: "I believe that to promote friendly relations between our countries, we naturally need to continue the economic exchange currently under way, but also to promote exchange on many other levels as well. Cultural exchange is particularly important, I think, because it contributes to mutual understanding. From that perspective, your visit to the Soviet Union is extremely significant."

Shin'ichi was particularly anxious to discuss the subject of fate with Mr. Sholokhov, because he had been deeply moved by the writer's novel *The Fate of a Man*. It told the story of a youth, Andrei Sokolov, who joined the Red Army during the time of civil war following the Russian Revolution. While Andrei was off fighting, his parents and sister died of starvation during a famine, leaving Andrei all alone.

He finds a job and works hard, eventually marrying and having three healthy children. But the outbreak of World War II tears the family apart. Andrei, who joins the army to defend his homeland, is captured by the Germans and put in a labor camp. He escapes, but is recaptured and placed under heavy security. On one occasion, he is almost executed when an informer among the prisoners tells the guards that Andrei has complained about the work.

Later, he attempts another escape, and this time he succeeds, making his way to safety among the Russian forces. He soon learns, however, that his wife and two of his children were killed two years earlier when a German bomb struck their house. His surviving child, his eldest son, has enlisted in the army, but his whereabouts are unknown. Then Andrei receives a letter from his son. Just before they are about to be reunited, the son is shot and killed by a German sniper. All of Andrei's hopes are dashed by his incredibly cruel fate.

Life is a struggle against suffering. We shine as human beings when we take on that struggle and triumph over our troubles. In other words, our fate, whatever form it takes, provides us with an opportunity to bring forth our true inner light.

While in this despairing state, Andrei meets a boy named Vanya who has been orphaned by the war, and he decides to take the child in and raise him. Vanya also comes to love Andrei and remains constantly by his side. At the end of the story, this father and adopted son walk off together, brimming with hope, to begin again somewhere new.

IN *The Fate of a Man*, the hero Andrei Sokolov finds a new purpose in life when, after enduring the most terrible tribulations, he decides to care for the orphan Vanya. Having a purpose gives us hope, and as long as we have hope, we can face anything that fate may deal us. But leading a meaningful life always involves effort and hardship. This is particularly so when it comes to raising others. In his writing, Mr. Sholokhov seems to be saying that our life's true purpose is found in living for the sake of others. Tolstoy wrote, "The only certain happiness in life is to live for others."[27]

The exclusive pursuit of one's own interests is not true happiness. It is by striving for the welfare of others that the great path to genuine happiness is opened.

The death toll in the Soviet Union during World War II is estimated to have been around twenty million people. There were countless Sokolovs and Vanyas everywhere throughout the country. And Mikhail Sholokhov lost his own mother in a German bomb attack. She had been born in a farming family, but both her parents died when she was a child. Her life was very hard. She had to work and had no opportunity to receive an education. She finally learned to read and write when her son Mikhail was a student at a distant junior high school because she wished to correspond with him. The author said she was a passionate woman.

Soon after Mr. Sholokhov entered junior high school, the German forces invaded Russia and started advancing toward the town where the school was, so he returned to his hometown. This was during World War I. The end of that war was followed by the Russian Revolution and then civil war. This uninterrupted strife forced him to give up his schooling. He studied on his own, however, and worked at many different jobs, including as an instructor teaching adults to read, a food supplier, a census taker, a porter, a clerical worker and a newspaper reporter. As a supporter of the Soviet government, he also participated in political activities.

When his masterwork, *And Quiet Flows the Don* was published, some in his hometown accused him of antirevolutionary activities. It was around this time that he was also accused of plagiarizing the book. He lived a turbulent life filled with struggle and hardship, which is precisely why his writing shines with lasting brilliance.

BRINGING UP the subject of Mr. Sholokhov's *The Fate of a Man*, Shin'ichi asked: "It may seem that a person's fate can be changed by modifying their environment or circumstances, but when you think seriously about what is actually required to change one's fate, it seems to me that the issue of self-transformation cannot be overlooked. What do you think?"

Mr. Sholokhov nodded and said: "That's true. I believe that our convictions are what determine whether we are controlled by fate. People who are not committed to reaching any firm goals are essentially powerless. We are all the creators of our own happiness. Realizing happiness comes down to how much we have forged ourselves spiritually. Those who have inner fortitude can move their lives in a positive direction even when confronted with the vagaries of fate."

Leaning forward in his seat, Shin'ichi said: "I agree completely. Buddhism teaches how to build the strongest and most elevated self in order to triumph over even fate's cruelest hand. We call this highest state of being Buddhahood, and the process of transforming ourselves human revolution. Buddhism views life as eternal and teaches that our accumulated past thoughts and actions are what create our present karma or fate. Therefore, we can change our future destiny by how we live now. In Buddhism, our actions in the present are everything."

Mr. Sholokhov listened intently as Shin'ichi spoke. He

was one of the great writers of the Soviet Union, a communist nation, but he agreed completely with Shin'ichi on the importance of the human being and the vital need for inner transformation.

The philosophies and lives of those who are masters of the art of living are always essentially in agreement with the teachings of Buddhism. In the depths of their lives, such individuals are yearning for the Buddhist Law. As Nichiren Daishonin says of the sages who dedicated their lives to the people's welfare, "Though the adherents of the non-Buddhist scriptures were unaware of it, the wisdom of such men contained at heart the wisdom of Buddhism" (WND-1, 1122).

SHIN'ICHI FURTHER inquired, "What's been the most difficult thing you've faced in life?"

Gazing into the distance, Mr. Sholokhov said: "As you grow older, it becomes harder and harder to remember the difficult times. You forget the details about various events and all your experiences, both the happy and the sad, become distant memories. When you're seventy years old, you'll understand what I'm saying."

In these remarks, Shin'ichi perceived the state of serenity and self-assurance that the great writer had achieved.

No matter how much wealth or fame we acquire, we are bound to end up in pitiful and unhappy circumstances if we're still obsessed with past angers and hatreds in our final years. Life's true victors are those who succeed in elevating their life-state to the point where they can embrace all people with compassion and love. In mountain climbing, when one reaches the summit's peak, one is filled with joy and satisfaction, and the hardship of the strenuous climb is forgotten. Similarly, when we transform our state of life, a refreshing joy and fulfillment pervade our being.

There was much that Shin'ichi still wished to ask the author and discuss with him. Not wanting to tire Mr. Sholokhov, however, he decided to bring their meeting to a close. As they parted, the writer shook Shin'ichi's hand firmly and said: "Let's meet again. Next May, I'll be seventy years old. I would be delighted to see you again then."

On leaving the apartment, Shin'ichi and the others were approached by a group of children playing nearby. They were all adorable, with shining, smiling eyes. Shin'ichi felt as if he were seeing incarnations of the little boy Vanya from Mr. Sholokhov's story *The Fate of a Man*. It occurred to him that it was the responsibility and duty of all adults to ensure that these children enjoyed a

bright and happy future, in the same spirit with which the story's hero Sokolov had cared for the orphaned Vanya. He said to them: "I'm from Japan. I came here to build a bridge to peace. Let's take a photo together."

With a cry of delight, the children joined Shin'ichi for a photograph. The autumn breeze caressed the trees lining the streets.

ON THE EVENING of September 16, after his meeting with Mikhail Sholokhov, Shin'ichi and Mineko hosted a dinner at a restaurant in Moscow to thank their Russian friends. They invited two hundred fifty people who had helped them deepen and strengthen bilateral relations between Japan and the Soviet Union, including Rector Rem Khokhlov of Moscow State University, Vice Chairperson E. V. Ivanov of the Union of Soviet Societies for Friendship and Cultural Relations with Foreign Countries, Vice President Ivan Kovalenko of the Soviet-Japan Society, Minister Vyacheslav Yelyutin of Higher and Secondary Specialized Education, First Deputy Minister of Culture V. F. Kukharskii and First Deputy Mayor of Moscow V. P. Isaev.

Shin'ichi and his party were scheduled to return to Japan the next evening. He and Mineko stood at the entrance to the restaurant to welcome the guests, smiling warmly and firmly shaking each person's hand in sincere appreciation.

The dinner began with opening remarks from Shin'ichi. He expressed his profound gratitude for the warm welcome he had received everywhere he went in the Soviet Union. He also conveyed his belief that broad and deep ties contributing to solid mutual understanding and bilateral cultural and educational exchange had been achieved during his trip. "I am confident," he said, "that those ties will expand and eventually grow into a network linking the hearts of the people of our two nations, becoming a golden alliance of friendship toward peace.

"At the same time, I will do my utmost throughout my life to convey to people back home the warm goodwill of all of you and promote a fair understanding of your nation, which plays such a pivotal role in world peace."

Shin'ichi then offered a toast to the happiness of the Soviet people and good relations between the two countries.

Friendly conversation among the guests ensued, and Shin'ichi and Mineko walked around the room cordially greeting and thanking everyone in person. A certain high-ranking official said to Shin'ichi, "Our nation made a major diplomatic error." In response to Shin'ichi's puzzled expression, the official continued, "We erred in not inviting you to the Soviet Union sooner, which has delayed the realization of cultural exchange between our two nations."

The official laughed heartily. In their many talks, they had established a relationship that permitted this friendly joking. Friendship is born through establishing heart-to-heart bonds.

AN IMPORTANT Soviet government official asked Shin'ichi, "Do you have any complaints after having spent time here in the Soviet Union, President Yamamoto?

"I do!" Shin'ichi responded. "I most certainly do!" When Shin'ichi's remark was translated into Russian, the official looked worried.

But Shin'ichi smiled and said: "I'm 99.9 percent satisfied with my visit, but I do have a 0.1 percent dissatisfaction. And precisely because I am so satisfied overall, this particular thing is especially troubling. My complaint is that you're all too big. When I try to embrace you in friendship, my arms aren't long enough to reach around and hug you!"

When the interpreter had finished translating his remark, the official burst out in hearty laughter.

The French author Victor Hugo wrote, "Laughter is sunshine; it chases winter from the human face."[28] When we can laugh heartily with someone, it's a sure sign of friendship. Openhearted laughter is a flower blooming in the rich soil of trust.

Everyone present had become good friends. They were all members of the same human family.

Addressing the gathering, Minister of Higher and Secondary Specialized Education Vyacheslav Yelyutin shared his impression of his meeting with Shin'ichi, saying: "I felt as if we were on the same page even before we had finished our initial exchange of greetings. We almost completely agreed on every educational issue." Stressing the importance of international cooperation in the field of education, the minister added: "We are looking forward expectantly to furthering friendly exchange between our countries. Please communicate that to the people of Japan."

Rector Khokhlov of Moscow State University also

rose to say a few words, at the end of which he raised his glass in a toast, saying: "President Yamamoto is an individual who deserves our sincerest respect. I'd like to propose a toast to President Yamamoto, to the Soka Gakkai that he leads and to friendship between the Soviet Union and Japan!" He then called out, "*Bolshoi kampai!*" *Bolshoi* is Russian for "great" or "big," and *kampai* is the Japanese word for "cheers" when giving a toast, so that *Bolshoi kampai* was his way of emphasizing his toast. This "Russian-Japanese" expression had been coined during Shin'ichi's visit as an expression of bilateral friendship.

Shin'ichi's last night in Moscow was spent amid friendship and genial conversation.

AT ONE POINT during the dinner, Soviet-Japan Society Vice President Ivan Kovalenko said to Shin'ichi: "I have some good news for you, President Yamamoto. Soviet Premier Aleksey Kosygin would like to meet with you tomorrow morning, September 17, at ten."

Shin'ichi had hoped to have the opportunity to meet the premier, as there were many things he wished to discuss with him for the sake of world peace. He was especially interested in communicating that China's leaders were earnestly seeking peace.

But the premier was of course very busy, and Shin'ichi understood that a meeting might well not materialize. He was already considering how and to whom else he might transmit his message concerning China. When he heard that in fact he would be able to meet Premier Kosygin, he accepted immediately, saying that he looked forward to paying his respects.

A fresh autumn breeze was blowing in Moscow the next day. Shin'ichi set off for the Kremlin shortly after half past nine in the morning for his meeting with Premier Kosygin. It had been decided that only he and one other member of his party would attend. At ten, when Shin'ichi stepped into the meeting room, Premier Kosygin was there waiting for him. Under his creased brow, the premier's gaze was sharp and his lips were pressed together in a firm expression. All in all, he gave the impression of a strong-willed individual who shouldered his heavy responsibilities as leader of the Eastern bloc—a role he shared with Soviet General Secretary Leonid Brezhnev—with gravity and seriousness.

Premier Kosygin was seventy years old, yet he exuded a youthful vitality—a crucial quality for any leader committed to blazing fresh trails.

Smiling, Shin'ichi reached out to shake the premier's hand and said: "Thank you so much for taking time out of your busy schedule to see me. I am deeply honored to be able to meet you."

The premier also smiled and said, "I've been looking forward to meeting you, too."

"I am humbled," Shin'ichi replied. "I wish to express my heartfelt gratitude for your kind support during this visit, thanks to which I received a wonderfully warm welcome everywhere I went."

The premier in turn highly commended Shin'ichi's trip, remarking that his efforts to engage others in dialogue for the sake of world peace and to deepen exchange between their nations had profound significance.

WHEN THE GREETINGS were over, Shin'ichi and Premier Kosygin sat down on either side of the meeting table facing each other. Vice President Ivan Kovalenko of the Soviet-Japan Society and Vice Chairperson E. V. Ivanov of the Union of Soviet Societies for Friendship and Cultural Relations with Foreign Countries sat on the premier's left, while interpreter and Moscow State University senior lecturer Leon Strijak sat on his right. The *Seikyo Shimbun* photographer and others accompanying Shin'ichi had to withdraw at this point.

Shin'ichi leaned forward and said, "May I speak frankly?" The premier nodded, and Shin'ichi continued: "I learned a lot about your country on this visit. I've learned that you are working earnestly to diminish international tensions, which I regard as very admirable. Unfortunately, however, the Soviet Union's commitment in this arena is not being communicated to Japan. While Japanese people may be familiar with Russian literature and folk songs, they don't have positive feelings toward the Soviet Union. Instead, many perceive it as a country to be feared.

"If you are genuinely interested in conveying the truth about your nation and gaining the understanding of the majority of Japanese people, it's crucial to make an effort to engage in much broader exchange with our nation, not limited to meeting solely with pro-Soviet government leaders and a few select groups or organizations. It's vital to actively reach out to conservative Japanese politicians and people who feel an aversion to the Soviet Union. True friendship cannot be built exclusively through political and economic exchange. I believe that cultural exchange is of utmost importance."

Shin'ichi spoke on the basis of his conviction that the Japan–Soviet relationship must be built on strong and solid ties of trust and exchange on various levels. Toward that end, it was vital to forge multilayered ties not only on an official level, but on a private level as well. As Tolstoy observed, it is the principle of reciprocity that leads to human progress.[29]

Aware of the possibility that his frankness might be misinterpreted as rude, Shin'ichi nevertheless shared his thoughts openly with the premier.

When Shin'ichi had finished speaking, Premier Kosygin replied: "I agree. We will take your opinions into consideration in our future steps in that direction."

OBSERVING PREMIER Kosygin's sincerity and willingness to listen to the opinions of others, Shin'ichi knew that he was in the presence of a man of high caliber. "Here is someone I can talk to!" he felt.

Shin'ichi continued: "In order to open a new path of exchange between our countries, I think it's important for you and General Secretary Brezhnev to visit Japan. Do you have any plans to do so?" He asked this crucial question with no preface or hesitation, believing that frank dialogue was the foundation for true human diplomacy.

The Japanese government was also very interested to know when the Soviet leaders might visit Japan. In October of the previous year, 1973, Japanese Prime Minister Kakuei Tanaka had visited the Soviet Union, and the leaders of the two countries agreed to continue negotiating a peace treaty. But no concrete plans for a visit by a top Soviet leader to Japan had yet materialized.

Premier Kosygin began to speak: "I plan to go to Japan. Both General Secretary Brezhnev and Chairman of the Supreme Soviet Nikolai Podgorny have indicated their desire to go there, too. We won't be able to do so within this calendar year, but we are presently considering a possible date.

"We wish to make every effort to complete a peace treaty with Japan. Toward that end, negotiations are currently taking place between our foreign ministers. I believe that the best opportunity for a visit by a top Soviet leader is after an agreement has been reached on the outstanding issues regarding that treaty." Premier Kosygin went on to speak forcefully and at great length about his thoughts on the treaty.

When the premier came to a pause in his comments, Shin'ichi interjected politely: "As far as the peace treaty between our nations is concerned, I hope that you will carry on extensive discussions with the Japanese foreign minister and other appropriate government authorities. But the Soka Gakkai is a Buddhist organization, and our concern for world peace is based on our religious convictions." Shin'ichi wanted to be certain that the premier understood the distinction between the position and perspective of the Soka Gakkai, a religious organization, and the Clean Government Party, a political one.

It is important to have the courage to say what needs to be said when it needs to be said. Vagueness is a fatal error that eventually leads to serious misunderstandings. As Dostoyevsky warned, most of the misfortunes of this world are caused by misunderstandings and insufficient explanations. Failing to communicate fully, he said, can cause great harm.[30]

SHIN'ICHI CONTINUED: "I founded the Clean Government Party, but it is completely independent from the Soka Gakkai both financially and in terms of personnel affairs. As such, I do not and cannot involve myself in the party, and all political matters are left to the party to handle.

"Both the Soka Gakkai and the Clean Government Party do share the fundamental goal of the happiness and peace of humanity. However, given that one is a religious group and the other a political group that must deal with the ever-changing circumstances of reality, their positions are different, and there may be times when they disagree on concrete policies that should be adopted. In addition, the kind of exchange we of the Soka Gakkai are seeking to promote is not political exchange but a broader flow of cultural and educational exchange on the level of ordinary citizens."

Shin'ichi then went on to talk about the history of the Soka Gakkai, explaining how it had fought against persecution by the Japanese militarist authorities during World War II. He further introduced how the organization had expanded its network for peace around the globe.

Nodding in quiet acknowledgement, Premier Kosygin asked Shin'ichi: "You are a Buddhist who has founded the Clean Government Party and a university. What is your basic ideology?"

Shin'ichi replied unhesitatingly, "I believe in peace, culture and education—the underlying basis of which is humanism."

When this was interpreted, the premier gave a smile that conveyed his deep satisfaction.

Shin'ichi's basic aim in life was to realize peace and happiness for all humanity based on the Buddhist philosophy of the sanctity of life. It was to enable people to polish and develop their lives and to build a vibrant, productive society. This is the meaning of kosen-rufu and of "establishing the correct teaching for the peace of the land." But conveying that purpose in such specialized Buddhist terms most likely wouldn't translate.

During his wartime imprisonment, Josei Toda awakened to the reality that the Buddha is life itself, and, upon his release, he set out to explain Buddhism in contemporary, easily intelligible terms that related directly to people's lives. Through his efforts, Mr. Toda was able to make Buddhist principles relevant to today.

Only when our thoughts and ideas based on Buddhism are expressed in ways that are accessible to people in contemporary society can they be persuasive and gain the understanding and acceptance of others.

AFTER HEARING Shin'ichi's basic philosophy, Premier Kosygin began to speak in a resonant voice: "I appreciate your philosophy. We need to realize those ideals here in the Soviet Union as well. You stated that you are an advocate of peace. All our actions are based on the fundamental position that we value peace and will not initiate hostilities."

The conversation was moving toward the subject Shin'ichi most wanted to discuss. He began to speak with enthusiasm: "That's wonderful. Hostilities must be avoided at all cost. I visited the Piskarevskoye Memorial Cemetery in Leningrad and I will never forget the tremendous number of innocent lives that the Soviet Union lost in World War II. During this trip, I have acquired a keen appreciation of just how earnestly the Soviet people and leaders long for peace."

A powerful outrage against war burned in Shin'ichi's heart. Reflecting on the bitter experiences of the people of Leningrad, so many of whom had been killed in the fierce attacks by German forces on their city, or whom had died of hunger or cold during the long siege, he spoke of his feelings upon his visit to the cemetery: "The Soviet people underwent a terribly cruel experience. This must not be allowed to happen ever again."

When Shin'ichi said this, a glint appeared in the premier's eyes. He watched intently as Shin'ichi spoke. Shin'ichi asked, "Where were you during World War II?"

Mr. Kosygin replied softly, "I was in Leningrad during the German siege." He stopped and was silent for a moment. He seemed to be recalling that time.

Anyone who has known the horror of war is loath to repeat the experience. As the great physicist Albert Einstein (1879–1955) declared: "Let [us] leave to future generations the inestimable heritage of a world from which the brutalities of war have been banished forever. We can do this if we are determined."[31] This is the mission of everyone alive today.

A determination to build peace shone in Premier Kosygin's eyes.

FIXING HIS GAZE on the premier, Shin'ichi said with energy: "Just like the Soviet people, the

Chinese people wish only for peace. China has no intention of invading any other nation."

The conversation was reaching its most essential point. Shin'ichi believed that if he communicated the true feelings of the Chinese people and their vice premier Li Xiannian, with whom he had met on his visit to China three months earlier, Premier Kosygin would act wisely.

Tolstoy observed, "Powder and blood had not succeeded in solving the question which diplomats could not settle."[32]

The tensions had not been resolved. Moreover, with China and the United States moving toward the normalization of diplomatic relations, and with China and Japan also having restored their bilateral ties, the Soviet Union began to feel severely threatened. While China and the Soviet Union had tried to settle their differences through talks between representatives of the two nations, progress had been minimal, and considerable distrust remained on both sides.

Shin'ichi forthrightly communicated his impressions from his China visit to Premier Kosygin: "China's top leaders assured me that they have no intention of attacking any other country. But, fearing the possibility of a Soviet attack, they were digging bomb shelters and taking other precautions in preparation. They are anxiously observing your country's actions. Forgive my directness, but is the Soviet Union considering attacking China?"

Premier Kosygin looked sharply at Shin'ichi. Beads of perspiration stood out on his forehead. Then he spoke with resolve: "No, the Soviet Union has no intention of attacking China. In terms of protecting the collective security of Asia as well, we have no desire to isolate China."

"I see," Shin'ichi said. "May I convey that to the leaders of China?"

PREMIER KOSYGIN was silent for a moment. Then he said in a decisive tone, "Please feel free to tell China's leaders that the Soviet Union will not attack their country."

Shin'ichi looked at the premier with a smile and said, "If that's the case, then why not be friends with China?"

The premier looked at a loss for words. Then, a warm smile spread across his face. The meeting of minds between the two men blossomed into smiles. Shin'ichi felt that this encounter had produced substantive results.

The American philosopher Ralph Waldo Emerson observed, "Wise, cultivated, genial conversation is the last flower of civilization and the best result which life has to offer us."[33] Dialogue can function like warm sunshine, melting frozen deadlocks and illuminating the future with hope.

The conversation moved on to nuclear weapons. Premier Kosygin said in a regretful tone, "There are more than enough nuclear weapons to destroy the world." In a soft but deeply resolved voice, he added: "If nuclear arms are allowed to proliferate, there is no telling what could happen should another Hitler appear. In such an event, we have no means to preserve global civilization. Sooner or later, the human race will have to opt for nuclear disarmament."

Shin'ichi could not conceal his astonishment at this statement. It was a groundbreaking declaration in that it ran completely counter to the Soviet Union's public position at the time that its nuclear arsenal was necessary to maintain world peace. It seemed to Shin'ichi to be a very courageous thing to say.

Premier Kosygin went on to share his thoughts about steps toward the total elimination of nuclear weapons, starting with banning nuclear testing. Shin'ichi agreed with him fully, and in fact he had strongly advocated the same ideas for some time. He felt a sense of joy at hearing the premier's words, thinking: "China also advocates the basic policy of the complete elimination of nuclear weapons. Clearly both the Soviet Union and China are in agreement on this issue. That means that a global shift toward nuclear abolition is a real possibility."

BASED ON Premier Kosygin's remarks, and strongly hoping that the Soviet Union would take the initiative in pushing for the elimination of nuclear weapons, Shin'ichi said: "I believe that in order to realize nuclear abolition, nations around the world, particularly those possessing such weapons, must establish a close relationship of trust. They need to reach out to one another and strive ceaselessly to foster that trust. As long as underlying mistrust and suspicion persist, it will be impossible to eradicate nuclear weapons. From that perspective, it is important for countries to continue engaging in exchange. It has been my consistent conviction that, in addition to political and economic exchange, exchange in the spheres of culture and education is also crucial."

The most vital key for the mutual prosperity of all humanity is transforming mistrust into trust.

Shin'ichi next posed a question: "The human race is

facing many serious challenges in the future—the nuclear issue we've been discussing, environmental destruction and feeding the world's population, among others. Do you think we can be optimistic about the twenty-first century?"

"We in the Soviet Union certainly hope for a bright future," the premier replied. "In fact, we have to make it so. Of course, I also believe that the time has come for humanity to reevaluate its actions up to now."

"I wholeheartedly agree," Shin'ichi said. "Humanity can no longer sustain a civilization based on mass production and mass consumption. There is not an unlimited supply of natural resources at our disposal. Unless we change our way of thinking, the human race is going to reach an impasse. In this regard, I have stressed the need for people to take note of the life philosophy of Buddhism that teaches the harmonious coexistence of humankind and nature."

Touching on the issue of food security, Shin'ichi then proposed, "In order to assist those who are refugees due to regional conflicts and those who are facing famine because of droughts or floods, I would like to suggest the formation of a World Food Bank."

"Yes, that's a very important idea," Premier Kosygin replied. "But before we try to solve famine, humankind must first abandon all war."

Shin'ichi perceived in these words the premier's strong desire for peace.

PREMIER KOSYGIN spoke with earnest conviction, as if articulating his most deeply held beliefs: "If humanity would focus on preparing for peace instead of war, we could redirect the present enormous expenditures and effort being channeled into weapons production into further food production. Peace is the way to solve problems surrounding famine."

Great leaders have weighty insights. Shin'ichi felt as if he had gained some understanding of Premier Kosygin's inner spirit.

Their meeting had already lasted ninety minutes, no doubt running much longer than the premier had anticipated, and Shin'ichi didn't want to take up any more of his time. "Thank you so much for making time in your busy schedule to meet me today," he said finally.

Premier Kosygin replied: "I found our exchange extremely worthwhile, and I appreciate having this opportunity to talk with you. The issues you raised are all important, and I'm sure your thoughts on these topics will have a strong influence not just on political and economic matters but on all the many problems we face."

At the close of their meeting, Shin'ichi presented the premier with various gifts, including a Japanese painting. Premier Kosygin gave him a silver medal commemorating the fiftieth anniversary of the Soviet Union. When they parted, the premier grasped Shin'ichi's hand firmly and said, "Let's meet again the next time you come to Moscow."

"Thank you," Shin'ichi replied. "I'm looking forward to it."

When they left the meeting room, Leon Strijak, Shin'ichi's interpreter, said to him in excitement: I was deeply moved by your meeting. It was very productive."

Afterward, on hearing from Mr. Strijak about the

encounter, Moscow State University Rector Rem Khokhlov, who had been waiting for the meeting to end, shook Shin'ichi's hand vigorously and said: "I am overjoyed to hear about the content of your meeting. I think it was a perfect step in forging a broad path toward friendly relations between our two nations."

"Thank you," Shin'ichi replied. "We were able to have a frank and open dialogue. I was profoundly impressed by Premier Kosygin's commitment to peace and his personal character."

When we are sincere and courageous in our interactions with others, we can enjoy frank and open dialogue on the deepest level.

SOVIET PREMIER Aleksey Kosygin was also apparently deeply satisfied with his meeting with Shin'ichi and regarded it as very meaningful. Soviet-Japan Society Vice President Ivan Kovalenko, who had worked hard to make Shin'ichi's invitation to the Soviet Union a reality and had sat in on the meeting, later wrote: "After their meeting, Premier Kosygin turned to me and asked: 'Mr. Kovalenko, where did you meet such an exceptional Japanese? How did you come across him?'"

Mr. Kovalenko also shared that the premier had instructed him to maintain a close relationship with Shin'ichi, saying that if he encountered any problems at the Kremlin, he should call the premier directly.

It is also reported that after he returned home that evening, Premier Kosygin said to his daughter Lyudmila: "I met an extraordinary and very interesting Japanese today. I was happy to have had a most refreshing discussion, even though we spoke about complex issues."

The wheels of history seemed to have begun turning slowly but perceptibly through these efforts by Shin'ichi, who was acting as a private citizen. Not only did the path to a new, amicable relationship between Japan and the Soviet Union start to open, but a bridge spanning the wide gap caused by tensions between China and the Soviet Union was also being built. Persistent, dedicated, wholehearted efforts can move mountains.

After his meeting with Premier Kosygin, Shin'ichi went at noon to the Friendship Hall of the Union of Soviet Societies for Friendship and Cultural Relations with Foreign Countries. It had been decided that Shin'ichi and the Union would issue a joint communiqué affirming the progress made in cultural exchange between Japan and the Soviet Union during the Japanese delegation's visit and expressing both parties' intent to continue working further in that direction. The signing was attended by Union Chairperson Nina Popova, Soviet-Japan Society Vice President Ivan Kovalenko, Soviet-Japan Society Secretary-General Victor Ugrinovich and others.

Chairperson Popova and Shin'ichi sat at a table adorned with the flags of their two nations and signed the communiqué. The document detailed the steps that had been taken toward friendly bilateral exchange from September 8, the first day of Shin'ichi's visit, onward, and it asserted their shared commitment to "deepen mutual understanding between the people of Japan and the Soviet Union, strengthen neighborly relations, and expand cultural, scientific and educational exchange."

THE COMMUNIQUÉ concluded with the words: "We believe that the visit of this delegation to the Soviet Union has been meaningful and that the relationships forged throughout will serve to promote better future amicable relations between Japan and the Soviet Union, thereby playing an important role in strengthening peace throughout Asia and the world."

After the signing, Shin'ichi led a toast to bilateral friendship. *Bolshoi kampai!* he called out. Everyone followed suit in smiling unison.

Afterward, Chairperson Popova, looking deeply moved, said to the gathering: "My friends, President Yamamoto has initiated the first step in opening the way to Soviet–Japan friendship. Now we must take action. Let's strive to build friendly relations with our neighbors!"

Turning to Shin'ichi and Mineko she then added:

"Please remain well and active for many years to come, for the sake of the futures of both Japan and the Soviet Union. Don't overexert yourselves. You are very, very precious." Her words exuded a warm, motherly tone.

"Thank you so much," Shin'ichi said. "I am very touched by your sincere concern, my gentle but strong mother!" Chairperson Popova smiled and tears came to her eyes. Solid human bonds are formed when hearts come together.

After the signing of the communiqué with the Union of Soviet Societies for Friendship and Cultural Relations with Foreign Countries, Shin'ichi and his party returned to their lodgings at the Hotel Rossiya, where they were met by Japanese journalists. A press conference began immediately. Shin'ichi responded to the reporters' questions, speaking of his meetings with Premier Kosygin and author Mikhail Sholokhov, what he felt had been achieved on this visit and his impressions of the Soviet Union.

Shin'ichi and his group were scheduled to leave Moscow and return to Japan that evening. When the press conference ended, one of the young people traveling with him contacted the Soka Gakkai Headquarters in Tokyo to say that all their official events had been safely completed and that they expected to arrive at Haneda International Airport in Tokyo at about noon the following day, September 18.

Vice President Kiyoshi Jujo said with resolve on the phone: "I'm sorry about the other day. We are now fully prepared for Sensei's return."

EARLIER, WHILE the Japanese delegation was still in Leningrad, one of the youth representatives had called Vice President Kiyoshi Jujo at the Soka Gakkai Headquarters. During that conversation, Mr. Jujo, sounding rather tense, had asked if it would be possible for Shin'ichi to delay the date of his return to Japan. When asked why, he said with some hesitation: "We've heard that there may be problems at Haneda Airport. Anti-communist and anti-Soviet activists are waiting for Sensei's arrival there and may attempt to cause trouble."

The young man immediately conveyed this information to Shin'ichi.

"So they want to ambush me," Shin'ichi said. "From the time I resolved to build bridges of friendship between Japan and China and Japan and the Soviet Union, I've been aware that something like this might happen. Such efforts to open new frontiers tend to be fraught with danger, since they seek to break down the national and ideological barriers that divide humanity and pave the way to peace and friendship. But global peace cannot be achieved without a firm resolve to give one's life to the cause. How disgraceful that the Soka Gakkai Headquarters should allow itself to be swayed in this way!"

Shin'ichi himself was unshaken. Smiling, he then said: "When the general has declared that he's returning to the castle, you don't ask him to delay. That's not the way a battle is conducted. I'll be returning as planned."

"I understand!" the youth replied. He then conveyed the following message to Mr. Jujo: "Sensei says he will be returning to Japan as scheduled, so please take whatever measures are necessary to ensure that there are no problems."

"I see. All right, then," said Mr. Jujo, deeply touched by Shin'ichi's unwavering determination.

From that moment on, the Soka Gakkai's top leaders chanted Nam-myoho-renge-kyo in a spirit of unified resolve and did everything conceivably possible to assure that Shin'ichi's return went safely and without incident.

Back in their hotel room, Mineko said to Shin'ichi: "This visit to the Soviet Union has been a great success. It's all due to everyone chanting Nam-myoho-renge-kyo."

"That's so true," Shin'ichi said. "It's thanks to the chanting of our ten million members." And together, Shin'ichi and Mineko chanted in gratitude.

THAT EVENING, after packing their bags and before heading to the airport, the Japanese delegation attended a farewell dinner at the restaurant in their hotel. It was hosted by Moscow State University Vice Rector Vladimir Tropin, who had accompanied them throughout their visit. Also on hand were Senior Lecturer Leon Strijak, who had been their interpreter, and several of his Japanese-language students. The students had helped the Japanese visitors in numerous ways during their trip, staying at the hotel with them, assisting with luggage and travel, acting as guides and arranging for their meals and cars. Shin'ichi wished to thank the students sincerely for everything they had done, so when Mr. Strijak brought up the idea of a goodbye party, he gladly agreed to attend.

These gifted students were likely to play an important role in promoting amicable ties between their two countries in the future, and Shin'ichi thought of them as his young friends. Shin'ichi and his traveling companions had come up with nicknames for the students during the time they spent together. They called one student who was always organizing things Chief Cabinet Secretary, and they dubbed the student who always arranged for their cars Minister of Transport. The student who arranged for their meals was Food Minister, and the student who liaised with the news services was their Foreign Minister. The student in charge of their travel expenses, meanwhile, was called Finance Minister.

The students were very happy about the success of Shin'ichi's visit. One of them said: "President Yamamoto, you have made a remarkable contribution to the history of friendly relations between our countries. We are very proud to have been a part of this."

Shin'ichi stood up at the beginning of the dinner to convey his sincere gratitude. He said: "We've succeeded in building a bridge of friendship between Japan and the Soviet Union on this trip. All of you who have supported us behind the scenes played a pivotal role in that achievement. I would like to thank you and express my appreciation from the bottom of my heart. There is a wise saying in the East: 'Where there is unseen virtue, there will be visible reward' (WND-1, 907). Actions taken for the sake of good, though they may go unnoticed, are certain to benefit their doers. This is a very important philosophy for our lives."

The students all smiled and nodded in agreement.

MOSCOW STATE University Vice Rector Tropin then spoke with deep feeling about his impressions of Shin'ichi's visit to the Soviet Union, saying: "I wish that President Yamamoto could spend more time in our country. I cannot help but feel that his visit was too short. But in these brief ten days, strong connections have been forged between our two nations, and a foundation for peace has been laid. I am certain this trip to the Soviet Union will shine forever in the history of friendly bilateral relations. They could be called 'ten days that shook the world'!"

"Ten days that shook the world" was a reference to a famous work of the same title written by the American journalist John Reed about the November Revolution in 1917, when the new Soviet government was first established. The vice rector was comparing the importance of Shin'ichi's visit to the epic ten days that were chronicled in John Reed's book.

Next, one of the youth division representatives in Shin'ichi's party stood up to say a few words. He wanted those present to understand the truth about Shin'ichi as a person and the true meaning of his actions.

"I would like to share my honest feelings with you today," he began. "Whenever I travel the world with President Yamamoto, I am always struck by the intensity of his desire for peace for all humankind and the earnestness of his struggle to create a world without war. For example, I think you have all witnessed this for yourself, but every night during this trip, the lights were still on in President Yamamoto's room at one and two in the morning. Why? Because he has been diligently writing in order to convey the reality of the Soviet people and their love of peace to people throughout Japan and around the globe.

"When President Yamamoto returns to Japan, he has a slew of meetings and other events waiting for him to attend. You cannot begin to imagine how densely packed his schedule is. Every moment is crucial. I for one am deeply moved and impressed by the incredible sincerity and earnestness of his actions."

Everyone applauded heartily. It seemed that those on the Soviet side who had observed Shin'ichi on this trip wholly shared these sentiments.

SHIN'ICHI INTERRUPTED the young man's unexpected remarks: "You shouldn't be talking about me. You should be thanking the others here."

"I'm sorry," the youth replied, "but I couldn't help myself."

He then continued: "Of course, I'll never forget the wonderful efforts of everyone here tonight who worked so hard to make President Yamamoto's visit to the Soviet Union a success. I know that the lights have been on in your rooms until two or three in the morning as well. I'd like to offer a toast to our unsparing joint efforts for peace. *Bolshoi kampai!*"

The voices of everyone present rang out in unison. Working together for their shared goal had warmed their hearts to one another and linked them in the desire for peace.

The time came to say goodbye. Autumn in Moscow had passed in a flash. When the delegation had arrived ten days earlier, the season was just beginning, but during their stay, the birch and poplar leaves had changed colors day by day. Now the air was so cold that their breath came out in puffs of white.

Shin'ichi and his party were seen off at the airport in Moscow by Moscow State University Rector Rem Khokhlov and his wife; Union of Soviet Societies for Friendship and Cultural Relations with Foreign Countries Vice Chairperson E. V. Ivanov; several of the students who had assisted them on their trip; and many other well-wishers.

Mr. Khokhlov and Shin'ichi continued to speak even as they stood at the foot of the stairway leading up to the plane.

"I'll never forget all you've done for us," Shin'ichi said. "Please come to Japan and visit Soka University and the Soka schools. Let's carry on our dialogue then. Let's keep working together to promote educational and cultural exchange between our two countries and stir up a great groundswell for peace. Our friendship is eternal. True friendship always stands the test of time. I will continue to watch over the students who assisted us on this trip as long as I live."

Looking deeply moved, Mr. Khokhlov shook Shin'ichi's hand firmly.

Shin'ichi added, as if declaring his heartfelt determination, "Now all we have to do is demonstrate our words through action!"

Determination without action is nothing but a lie. A pledge only becomes reality when acted upon. A person of integrity is a person of action.

SHIN'ICHI'S PLANE took off around eight in the evening on September 17. As he looked down at the lights of Moscow below, Shin'ichi thought: *I was able to plant many seeds of friendship on this trip. Now I must continue to promote exchange and with great sincerity foster those seeds into towering trees of friendship.*

Nichiren Daishonin writes: "You cannot strike fire from flint if you stop halfway" (WND-1, 319). Perseverance is also important in friendship. Friendship cannot grow if interaction stops with a single meeting.

The Soviet people earnestly long for peace, thought Shin'ichi, *and Premier Kosygin came right out and said that the Soviet Union will not attack China. I must visit China again and convey that message to the Chinese leadership. I must also communicate the thoughts and feelings of the Soviet top leaders and people not only to China but to Japan and the entire world.*

From then on, Shin'ichi gave his all to putting this determination into action. A little more than a month after his return to Japan, the articles about the Soviet Union he had started writing during his visit for various newspapers and magazines not affiliated with the Soka Gakkai had reached the volume of a book. He had been writing feverishly, whenever he could find a spare moment.

When Moscow State University Senior Lecturer Leon Strijak and some of his students visited Japan in early October, Shin'ichi invited them to Soka University, the Kyushu General Training Center (the present-day Twenty-first Century Nature Conference Center) in Kagoshima Prefecture[34] and other places, deepening the ties of friendship with them. This time, Shin'ichi arranged for their meals and travel, wishing to reciprocate for all they had done during his stay in the Soviet Union.

At the end of October, Moscow State University Rector Rem Khokhlov, his wife and other university representatives came to Japan. Shin'ichi met with them at Soka University, the Seikyo Shimbun Building and the Soka Gakkai Headquarters, where they discussed future plans for educational exchange. In one conversation just before Mr. Khokhlov's return to the Soviet Union, Shin'ichi entrusted him with a letter for Premier Kosygin. The rector also expressed his wish that they could meet again in Moscow the following spring.

The tide of friendship had begun to flow powerfully toward the vast ocean of the twenty-first century, destined eventually to grow into an enormous groundswell of education, culture and peace.

Shin'ichi urged himself on to open the way to a brighter future, to pioneer new frontiers, courageously and fearlessly, for as long as he lived.

The great Russian dramatist Anton Chekhov wrote in one of his plays, "Sow the seeds of wisdom, of goodness, of eternity!"[35]

Notes:

1. Alexander Pushkin, "To the Poet," *The Poems, Prose and Plays of Alexander Pushkin,* compiled and edited by Avrahm Yarmonlinsky (New York: The Modern Library, 1936), p. 71.

2. Translated from Japanese. Plato, *Puraton zenshu* (Collected Works of Plato), translated by Aritsune Mizuno and Koichi Nagasaka (Tokyo: Iwanami Shoten, 1975), vol. 14, p. 72.

3. This article appeared in the September 8, 1994, issue of the *Seikyo Shimbun,* the Soka Gakkai daily newspaper.

4. Translated from Japanese. I. A. Gruzdev, *Jinrui no kyoshi 4—Goriki* (Gorky—Teacher of Humanity, Series 4), translated by Fusaji Yamamura (Tokyo: Meiji Tosho Shuppan, 1972), p. 319.

5. Translated from Japanese. Fyodor Dostoyevsky, "Roshia bungaku ni tsuite no ichiren no hyoron" (A Series of Essays on Russian Literature), in *Dosutoefusuki zenshu* (Collected Writings of Dostoyevsky), translated by Fumihiko Konuma (Tokyo: Chikuma Shobo, 1981), vol. 20-A, p. 61.

6. Translated from Russian. M. V. Lomonosov, *Stikhotvoreniya* (Poems) (Leningrad: Sovetskii pisateli, 1954).

7. Translated from Russian. N. Sovetov, *Jajda poznaniya* (Thirst for Knowledge) (Moscow: Molodaya gvardiya, 1986).

8. See Mahatma Gandhi, *The Collected Works of Mahatma Gandhi* (New Delhi: The Publications Division, Ministry of Information and Broadcasting, Government of India, 1995), vol. 87, p. 295.

9. Bertrand Russell, *Education and the Social Order* (London: George Allen and Unwin Ltd., 1932), p. 27.

10. Rabindranath Tagore, *The English Writings of Rabindranath Tagore*, edited by Sisir Kumar Das (New Delhi: Sahitya Akademi, 1996), vol. 3, p. 725.

11. Translated from Japanese. Maksim Gorky, *Goriki: Jido bungaku ron* (Gorky: On Children's Literature), edited by N. B. Medvedeva, translated by Masanobu Togo and Keiji Kasama (Tokyo: Shinhyoron Co., Ltd., 1973), p. 396.

12. Hall Caine, *The Eternal City* (New York: D. Appleton and Company, 1901), p. 289.

13. Rabindranath Tagore, *The English Writings of Rabindranath Tagore,* vol. 2, p. 413.

14. Leo Tolstoy, *The Kingdom of God Is Within You—Christianity Not As a Mystic Religion But As a New Theory of Life,* translated by Constance Garnett (Lincoln, Nebraska: University of Nebraska Press, 1984), p. 342.

15. Translated from Russian. *Velikie misli velikikh lyudei* (Great Thought of Great People), edited by I. I. Komarova and A. P. Kondrashov (Moscow: Ripol Classic, 1998), vol. 3, p. 345.

16. Harrison E. Salisbury, *The 900 Days: The Siege of Leningrad* (New York: Harper and Row, Publishers, 1969), p. 484.

17. Leo Tolstoy, *War and Peace,* translated by Rosemary Edmonds (London: Penguin Books, 1978), p. 715.

18. Harrison E. Salisbury, *The 900 Days: The Siege of Leningrad*, pp. 460–61.

19. http://www.arlindo-correia.com/040704.html (October 16, 2007).

20. Jean-Jacques Rousseau, *Discourse on the Sciences and Arts (First Discourse) and Polemics,* translated by Judith R. Bush, Roger D. Masters and Christopher Kelly (Hanover, NH: University Press of New England, 1992), p. 111.

21. Nikolai Gogol, *Dead Souls,* translated by D. J. Hogarth (Project Gutenberg Etext #1081) http://www.gutenberg.org/dirs/etext97/dsols10.txt> (October 17, 2007).

22. Translated from Russian. L. N. Tolstoy, *Polnoe sobranie sochinenii* (Complete Works) (Moscow: Terra, 1992), vol. 45, p. 338.

23. Anton Tchekoff, *Plays,* translated by Julius West (New York: Charles Scribner's Sons, 1916), p. 162.

24. Leo Tolstoy, *A Confession and Other Religious Writings,* translated by Fane Kentish (London: Penguin Books, 1987), p. 68.

25. Translated from Japanese. Aleksandr Pushkin, *Pushikin zenshu* (The Collected Writings of Pushkin), translated by Kaori Kawabata and Tetsuo Yonekawa (Tokyo: Kawade Shobo Shinsha, 1973), vol. 5, p. 164.

26. Leo Tolstoy, *A Calendar of Wisdom,* translated by Peter Sekirin (New York: Scribner, 1997), p. 30.

27. Leo Tolstoy, *Short Novels: Stories of Love, Seduction, and Peasant Life,* selected and introduced by Ernest J. Simmons (New York: Modern Library, 1965), vol. 1, p. 142.

28. Victor Hugo, *Les Misérables,* translated by Lee Fahnestock and Norman MacAfee (New York: New American Library, 1987), p. 569.

29. Translated from French. Leo Tolstoy, *Tolstoy's Letters: 1880–1910,* selected, edited and translated by R. F. Christian (New York: Charles Scribner's Sons, 1978), vol. 2, p. 427.

30. Translated from Japanese. Fyodor Dostoyevsky, *Dosutoefusuki zenshu* (Collected Writings of Dostoyevsky), translated by Masao Yonekawa (Tokyo: Kawade Shobo Shinsha, 1973), vol. 19, p. 38.

31. Albert Einstein, *Einstein on Peace,* edited by Otto Nathan and Heinz Norden (New York: Avenel Books, 1981), p. 142.

32. Leo Tolstoy, *Sebastopol,* translated by Frank D. Millet (Ann Arbor, Michigan: The University of Michigan Press, 1961), p. 36.

33. Ralph Waldo Emerson, "Woman," *The Complete Works of Ralph Waldo Emerson* (Boston: Houghton, Mifflin and Company, 1900), vol. 11, p. 283.

34. Kyushu is the southernmost of Japan's four main islands.

35. Anton Chekhov, *Tchekhov's Plays and Stories,* translated by S. S. Koteliansky (London: J. M. Dent and Sons, Ltd., 1937), p. 163.

Ties of Trust

"AS GOOD SAID as done! Let's make a fresh start."[1] This impassioned cry of the Chinese author Lu Xun resonated powerfully in Shin'ichi Yamamoto's heart. Lu Xun also wrote, "In every age, there are stalwart champions who stand up as pioneers and forerunners to open and clear the way forward."[2] Embracing this spirit, Shin'ichi had pledged to become a pioneer in the effort to realize world peace.

In mid-November 1974, some two months after his return from the Soviet Union, Shin'ichi received a telegram via the Chinese Embassy in Tokyo inviting him to visit Peking University in Beijing. On his first visit to China six months earlier, he had presented Peking University with a list of five thousand Japanese-language books and other titles that he wanted to donate to its library as part of the Soka Gakkai's initiative to promote cultural exchange. Now the books had arrived in Beijing, and the university wished to conduct a presentation ceremony. The telegram conveyed the university's earnest hope that Shin'ichi would be able to attend the ceremony, stating, "We believe that your visit to China will further promote friendly relations between the people of China and Japan, as well as exchange between Peking University and Soka University."

Shin'ichi wished to visit China as soon as possible to convey to the Chinese leadership the message that Soviet Premier Aleksey Kosygin had imparted to him. He also felt that another visit to the country would be important in terms of furthering cultural exchange between Japan and China. He therefore accepted Peking University's kind invitation with gratitude.

Shin'ichi set out on this second trip to China on December 2. After arriving at Tokyo's Haneda International Airport at half past eight in the morning with his wife, Mineko, he chatted in an airport waiting room with one of the councilors from the Chinese Embassy in Tokyo and other well-wishers who had come to see them off. It was a cold morning and the wind was chilly. As they were talking, an airline representative came to inform them that it was snowing in Beijing. The councilor thanked Shin'ichi for traveling to China in the cold of winter.

"Neither snow nor bitter cold nor any other adverse circumstance can deter me from my course," Shin'ichi replied. "My commitment to Japan–China friendship will never change. I will forge ahead for that purpose with sincerity and integrity."

Nothing can stop a person of genuine commitment.

ON THIS TRIP, Shin'ichi was able to fly directly from Japan to China. There had been no direct flights between the two countries six months earlier, when he made his first visit. At that time, he and his party had to fly to the British territory of Hong Kong and take a train from Kowloon to Lo Wu, the last Hong Kong station before the Chinese border. From there, after walking on foot for about three hundred thirty feet to Shenzhen Station on the Chinese side, they boarded a train to Guangzhou, where they then caught a flight to Beijing. The entire journey had taken two days.

At the end of September, however, air routes linking Japan and China had been opened. Even so, there were only four flights a week to China, including only one direct flight a week to Beijing. The plane Shin'ichi and his party would be flying on would stop in Osaka and Shanghai before reaching its final destination of Beijing. Still, even with this relatively circuitous route, the entire journey would only take about seven hours.

Shin'ichi sensed how much the times had changed. Who could have imagined six years ago, when he first proposed the normalization of Japan–China diplomatic relations, that such an age would come?

The times move and change. But first, we have to move people's hearts. When people change, history changes without fail.

The hour of their departure arrived. Shin'ichi climbed

the stairs leading to his plane, turned and waved to those seeing him off and boarded. He was scheduled to spend four nights and five days in China this time, all of it in Beijing.

The plane took off from Haneda Airport a little before ten that morning, with a stopover first in Osaka, then Shanghai. The flight from Osaka to Shanghai was two-and-a-half hours and the last leg, from Shanghai to Beijing, another hour and a half.

During the flight, Shin'ichi thought deeply about ways to promote cultural and educational exchange between Japan and China. He also strove to show his appreciation to those who were doing so much to support his trip, and he presented one of the flight attendants with a book in which he had written on the flyleaf, "May happiness shine on you, an emissary of the skies flying between Japan and China."

True friendship starts with treasuring those we meet and forming ties of trust with them.

Shin'ichi and his party arrived in Beijing at half past four in the afternoon. It was below freezing in the city, and the wind pierced their cheeks like icy needles. But forging ahead, braving cold winds, was the very heart of Shin'ichi's commitment.

A NUMBER OF PEOPLE were waiting to greet Shin'ichi and his group at the airport in Beijing. They included a party from Peking University comprising top officials, the head librarian and faculty and student representatives; China-Japan Friendship Association Secretary-General Sun Pinghua and Council Member Jin Sucheng; and a secretary from the Japanese Embassy in

Beijing. Many of the smiling faces Shin'ichi saw before him were those of old friends.

One of the university officials expressed his deep appreciation for the large gift of books and especially thanked Shin'ichi for traveling to China to attend the presentation ceremony.

Shin'ichi replied: "I'm the one who is grateful for your kind invitation. And I'm also very glad that our donation to your library has been so well received. We will strive to make an even greater contribution to friendship between the people of Japan and China, as well as to promote exchange between Peking University and Soka University."

Shin'ichi then presented the officials with his newly published book *Chugoku no ningen kakumei* (*The Human Revolution in China*). It contained his writings describing his first visit to China. The official publication date was December 5, which was in three days' time, but he had brought advance copies to present to his Chinese friends.

Shin'ichi and his party then headed from the airport to their lodgings at the Beijing Hotel, arriving there close to six that evening.

China-Japan Friendship Association President Liao Chengzhi and his wife called on Shin'ichi shortly thereafter. Mr. Liao and Shin'ichi embraced, happy to see each other again after an interval of six months. Sun Pinghua and Jin Sucheng, who had met them at the airport, and Lin Liyun, the interpreter who had assisted them during their first visit, also joined them. An amicable conversation ensued in Shin'ichi's hotel room.

Shin'ichi said: "Thank you all so much for coming to

greet me so soon after my arrival. Since I was invited to China this time by Peking University, I was afraid I might not have the opportunity to see President Liao on this visit."

"Nothing could prevent me from seeing you when you come to China," Mr. Liao replied. "We are friends, after all."

Good faith is manifested through action; it is a matter of deeds, not words.

Shin'ichi was deeply touched by Mr. Liao's sentiment.

"To show my gratitude to you, President Liao," he said, "I will strive even harder to open a path of exchange among young people and create a shining future for our two countries."

Responding to sincerity with sincerity is the way to foster strong and enduring bonds with others.

HEARING SHIN'ICHI'S words, President Liao nodded and said with feeling: "I have the greatest admiration for your unwavering commitment to China–Japan friendship, President Yamamoto. I've been told by the Chinese ambassador to Japan that on this trip you will also be making a donation of books to Wuhan University."

"Yes," Shin'ichi said. "I would like to initiate exchange with as many Chinese universities as possible. In the case of Wuhan University, a particular Soka University student has been doing his utmost to open the way to exchange with the same commitment that I have to promoting friendship between the people of Japan and China, and I wish to support and show my appreciation for his tireless efforts."

President Liao smiled and said that it was wonderful to see such a strong bond existing between a university's founder and student, calling it a fine example of the joint commitment of mentor and disciple.

Mahatma Gandhi (1869–1948) declared, "A disciple is more than son."[3] This was a sentiment that Shin'ichi agreed with completely. It is the tradition of the Soka Gakkai that mentor and disciple work together in the same spirit to pave the way to peace and the happiness of humankind.

Shin'ichi began to discuss the events that had led up to his decision to donate books to Wuhan University. It had started with Shironobu Kurata, a member of Soka University's first graduating class. Inspired by Shin'ichi's 1968 call for the normalization of diplomatic relations between Japan and China, and believing that exchange with China was crucial for achieving peace in Asia and the world, Mr. Kurata formed the Soka University Chinese Studies Club.

In 1973, out of his desire to gain firsthand experience of China, Mr. Kurata also participated in a student delegation to the country that was sponsored by the Japan-China Friendship Association. At a welcome banquet at Wuhan University during that trip, he happened to be seated next to a Japanese-language instructor at the university named Wu Yue'e. Mr. Kurata spoke to her proudly about Soka University, explaining that, as a new university, it aimed to become the highest seat of humanistic education for the twenty-first century and took as its mission the realization of peace. He also urged her to visit Soka University if she should ever make a trip to Japan.

Ms. Wu apparently became quite interested in Soka University. Born in China, she had lost her father at an early age and was raised by her uncle, an overseas Chinese living in Japan. After World War II, she married Li Hanbo, a Chinese student who had come to Japan to study during the war, and they returned to China together. She secured a job in her homeland teaching Japanese, eventually finding a position as a Japanese-language instructor at Wuhan University, where she met Mr. Kurata at the welcome banquet.

IN SPRING of the following year, 1974, Shironobu Kurata wrote a letter to Wu Yue'e informing her of President Yamamoto's impending first visit to China. Ms. Wu, however, was in Japan caring for her sick uncle at the time, so her husband forwarded the letter to her. When she received it, she phoned Mr. Kurata.

"Since you're in Japan," the young man said to her during their conversation, "why don't you come to Soka University, and I'll show you around?"

Taking Mr. Kurata up on his offer, Ms. Wu visited Soka University in August. On that day, special summer lectures were being held on campus, and Shin'ichi, as university founder, was giving a commemorative address titled "On Life and Learning." In the evening, Shin'ichi was also scheduled to attend a gathering with Soka Gakkai student division members who were studying at Soka University. Mr. Kurata had informed the university in advance that he would be showing the Wuhan University instructor around the campus that day, and the information had been relayed to Shin'ichi.

After visiting the language laboratory and other facilities, Ms. Wu met with some of Soka University's Chinese language instructors and exchanged opinions on foreign language education with them. That evening, she was also invited to attend the student division meeting, which was being held outdoors on the university's athletic field. It was there that she met Shin'ichi for the first time. Sitting down beside her, Shin'ichi began to tell her about the warm welcome he and his party had received on their visit to China.

"Everyone was so kind to us," he said, "and we are deeply grateful. As a small token of our appreciation, we'd like to welcome you tonight in the same spirit. Let's work together to build a golden bridge of friendship linking our two countries."

Picking up the microphone at the end of the meeting, Shin'ichi announced to the assembled students that Wu Yue'e from Wuhan University was in attendance, and he asked everyone to offer three rousing cheers as an expression of their wish for lasting friendship between Japan and China. He and Ms. Wu then circled the field, listening to the students' cheers.

As they walked, Shin'ichi thought to himself, *This path of friendship has been opened through the earnest efforts of a Soka University student, and I'll do my best to ensure that it grows into a broad, expansive road.* Addressing Mr. Kurata in his heart, he pledged, "My young friend, your efforts will not go to waste!"

A mentor always strives to respond to his disciples' efforts with utmost sincerity.

SHIN'ICHI INVITED Ms. Wu to Soka University again in November, at which time they spoke over a meal about ways to establish lasting friendship between Japan and China. During this meeting, the subject of educational exchange between Soka University and Wuhan University also arose. Shin'ichi pondered making a donation of books to the latter university, just like that which had been made to Peking University. Before traveling to China on his second visit, he had expressed this intention to Chinese Ambassador to Japan Chen Chu.

After Shin'ichi finished explaining this series of events, China-Japan Friendship Association President Liao Chengzhi remarked: "I deeply appreciate your consideration. Your efforts are certain to broaden and strengthen the path of friendly relations between our two countries. I'm looking forward to seeing what the future brings."

The conversation grew livelier, and when Shin'ichi inquired about Mr. Liao's health, the latter smiled and replied: "People like me, who participated in the Long March, all have some physical ailment to contend with. But I regard it as proof of my struggle."

Shin'ichi, who himself had long been engaged in a selfless struggle, well understood Mr. Liao's feelings.

Madame Song Qingling, the wife of Sun Yat-sen, said that while struggle is always arduous and demanding, there can be no victory without it.[4]

Without such resolve, a great vow cannot be fulfilled. Shin'ichi said: "I know precisely what you're saying.

The health of my mentor, second Soka Gakkai president Josei Toda, was seriously damaged during the two years he spent in prison as a result of persecution by the militarist authorities. I believe his imprisonment was a major factor in his early death at the age of fifty-eight. But his spirit remained vigorous to the very end."

"I see," Mr. Liao remarked. "I believe that those who fight selflessly for the happiness of others experience true joy and satisfaction in life."

"Nevertheless, President Liao, I hope you will live a long and healthy life for the sake of friendship between our nations," Shin'ichi declared. "Please promise me you will! Living a long and healthy life is your new Long March. The struggle has just begun."

The two men smiled at each other warmly.

ALSO PRESENT during Shin'ichi's conversation with China-Japan Friendship Association President Liao and the others was Yin Lianyu, who had interpreted for Shin'ichi on his first visit to China. Mineko distributed small personal gifts to everyone gathered, giving Ms. Yin a handkerchief with a cat embroidered on it. She had purchased it especially for the interpreter, having learned on their previous visit to China that Ms. Yin liked cats. Mineko also presented her with a stuffed toy Persian cat that a young women's division member who had accompanied them on that first trip had sent for Ms. Yin. The young woman had also remembered the interpreter saying that she liked cats.

"How cute!" Ms. Yin exclaimed. "I'm so touched that you remembered my love for cats!"

Mineko also presented a Chinese-Japanese dictionary and a Japanese-Chinese dictionary along with a chronology of world history to a young man from the China-Japan Friendship Association who had traveled with them last time. Shin'ichi and the others had done their utmost to remember what their Chinese friends had shared about themselves, accordingly selecting gifts that they thought they would like. Each gift was an expression of their good wishes for the recipient. Thinking of things from the perspective of others is the foundation of true consideration.

While Ms. Yin and Mineko chatted animatedly, Shin'ichi invited Mr. Liao to a separate room to talk.

When they were alone, Shin'ichi said, carefully choosing his words: "As a matter of fact, I have something very important that I wish to relay to you. As I believe you know, in September I traveled to the Soviet Union and met with Soviet Premier Aleksey Kosygin. During our conversation, I told him that China had no intention of attacking any other country. I also told him about the bomb shelters the Chinese people were building throughout their cities in anticipation of a possible Soviet attack."

Mr. Liao gazed earnestly at Shin'ichi, waiting for his next words.

"I then asked him directly," Shin'ichi continued, "if the Soviet Union was planning to attack China. The premier clearly stated that his country had no intention of doing so and that, in terms of protecting the collective security of Asia as well, it had no desire to isolate China either. He also said that I could pass on his words to the Chinese leadership. I hope that you will do so for me."

Mr. Liao nodded vigorously, his eyes gleaming with excitement.

O N THE EVENING of December 2, the day that Shin'ichi and his party arrived in Beijing, Peking University held a welcome banquet for them at the Beijing Hotel, where they were staying.

During the dinner, one of the top officials of Peking University expressed his deep appreciation for the fact that Shin'ichi and his delegation had made the journey to Beijing to attend the presentation ceremony for the books that Shin'ichi had donated to the university library.

He then said: "President Yamamoto paid a friendship visit to our country at the end of May this year and, after returning to Japan, published many articles about his trip that have further contributed to promoting friendship and mutual understanding between the people of our two countries. These articles clearly demonstrate President Yamamoto's goodwill and friendly feelings toward the Chinese people."

Already during his first trip to China, wishing to present the truth about China not only to Japan but also to the entire world, Shin'ichi had begun writing articles and essays at the request of various newspapers and magazines not affiliated with the Soka Gakkai. After returning to Japan, he continued to write at a fevered pace, even cutting short his hours of sleep to do so. In the middle of the night, after all his other work was finished, he would sit down to write, sometimes to the point where his shoulders ached, his neck hurt, and he couldn't lift his arms. Still, he kept on writing.

The power of the pen is truly immense. Words can

dispel the darkness of falsehood, illuminate reality with the light of truth and cause the sun of courage to rise in people's hearts. One champion of words is equal to a great force a million strong.

At the thank-you dinner Shin'ichi had hosted in Beijing during his first visit to China, he had said, "Please watch our future actions!" His writings about China were one concrete manifestation of that pledge. The Chinese side had been paying attention to the efforts Shin'ichi had been making in this regard and held them in the highest esteem.

Shin'ichi now stood up to thank his hosts from Peking University at this banquet marking the start of his second visit to China.

After conveying his appreciation for the warm welcome he and his party had received, he began to share how the Soka Gakkai had set out as the Soka Kyoiku Gakkai (Value-Creating Education Society), an organization dedicated to educational reform, and how it had carried on the mission of contributing to the promotion and advancement of education.

Stressing the vital role of education, he added: "I have given my all for the sake of education, which I consider to be my life's work. This is because the aim of the Soka Gakkai is to promote peace and culture, and humanistic education is of central importance to that effort."

SHIN'ICHI CONTINUED to discuss the relationship between education and peace, saying: "The construction of lasting world peace; cooperation between peoples; reciprocity and equality between nations; and the creation of a society in which all people can live lives of true dignity—all of these endeavors rest on the foundation of education. I firmly believe that education is the wellspring of human culture that enriches society with fresh vitality and energy for dynamic progress."

Shin'ichi then began to talk about Soka University: "Soka University, which I founded, has three mottoes: 'Be the highest seat of learning for humanistic education'; 'Be the cradle of a new culture'; and 'Be a fortress of peace for humankind.' These mottoes are an expression of my hopes and aspirations that youth will always stand on the side of the people and open a bright new tomorrow, that they will always protect the people and contribute further to a peaceful world. I believe that Peking University shares this spirit.

"Based on this common goal of peace, we of Soka University pledge to make even greater efforts to promote educational exchange aimed at opening a new era so that successive generations of Japanese and Chinese youth will maintain and strengthen the ties of friendship forged by us today."

Peace is humanity's most cherished wish and dream, the realization of which should by rights be the most important mission of institutions of higher learning around the globe. No matter how outstanding a university is, if it only produces coldhearted, unfeeling elitists who don't care if the world's people are suffering from such injustices as war, famine, poverty and discrimination, then it has failed at the task of education. That is why humanistic education is essential. Education's fundamental purpose must always be to cultivate genuine humanity and to foster individuals of compassion and integrity.

Shin'ichi believed that in order to achieve peace and

other lofty goals, it was vital to bring together universities and students from around the globe. His idea of establishing a United Nations of Education was also aimed at building a network of students, transcending national and ideological boundaries, dedicated to creating world peace.

That evening, a lively discourse on the subjects of peace education and educational exchange occupied their conversation.

THE FOLLOWING day, December 3, Shin'ichi and his party attended the book presentation ceremony, held in the Russian Language Center of Peking University. The event was attended by some one hundred individuals, including top officials and student representatives of Peking University; President Liao Chengzhi and other members of the China-Japan Friendship Association; State Council members; Beijing City officials; and others.

"I am honored to present you with this heartfelt gift," said Shin'ichi, before handing a token number of books together with a complete list of all five thousand titles to a university representative. The room erupted in vigorous applause.

Shin'ichi then presented Peking University student representatives with a message from Soka University students and a collection of their research papers, as well as a tape of the first Chinese-language speech contest held at Soka University in October of that year. He also presented the children attending the Peking University Allied Elementary School with paintings, drawings and calligraphy made by Japanese elementary school students. None of the gifts were expensive, but they were perhaps the most appropriate kinds of gifts for promoting mutual understanding of one another's thoughts and ideas. Shin'ichi was thinking hard about how he could bring the hearts of the young people of Japan and China together.

In his remarks, Shin'ichi explained the sentiments behind his donation of books to the library, saying: "I am deeply moved that my small gesture of goodwill represented by this gift has been accepted by Peking University, a citadel of learning that has such an important role in the future of China, a nation that in turn has such a vital role in the future of humanity. I am equally moved that you are holding this fine ceremony to which you have so kindly invited my colleagues and me.

"This gift of books contains my sincere sentiment as an ordinary citizen who wishes for friendship and peace between the people of Japan and China. I will be profoundly gratified if these books serve some useful purpose to your school for many years to come and if they not only help your students but also become a tie of peace and friendship linking Japan and China."

Good books serve as spiritual sustenance for young people and are the best teachers to help them understand other cultures and the world. The Russian writer Leo Tolstoy (1828–1910) wrote, "Good books are a good influence."[5]

Shin'ichi clearly envisaged the day when the youth of Japan and China would gain a deep understanding of one another, develop strong bonds of friendship and advance together side by side. He was confident that such a time would indeed come.

DURING HIS remarks, Shin'ichi said that whenever he visited a country, he always specifically made a point of calling on educational institutions and meeting and talking with educators and students there. This was based on his conviction that education holds the key to humanity's future.

Shin'ichi then went on to share what had prompted him to make his proposal for the normalization of diplomatic relations between Japan and China at a student division meeting (in 1968). He said: "Friendship with China must be maintained no matter what. The horrible tragedy of World War II must never be repeated. As someone who has suffered the pain and grief of losing a close family member during that war, I have held this belief from the days of my youth.

"At that meeting of students, I said: 'I hope that, when you become society's leaders, the youth of Japan and China will be able to work together in harmony and friendship to build a bright new world. When all the peoples of Asia, with Japan and China leading the way, begin to assist and support one another, it will mark the start of an age when the dark clouds of poverty and the brutality that presently envelop much of the region will lift and the sun of hope and happiness will at last shine its rays upon all of Asia.'

"It was this conviction that led me to visit China. In addition, I have donated these books to your library because it is my fervent wish that through educational exchange, we will deepen our mutual understanding and work together toward a hope-filled future."

The students' eyes shone brightly. Shin'ichi's words drove home to them his impassioned commitment to friendship between Japan and China. They listened intently as he spoke.

In closing, he said, "For the bright futures of both our countries and for the sake of peace in Asia and the prosperity of humankind, I promise to work even more closely with all of you as we move forward to our goal."

Everyone applauded enthusiastically, their faces filled with emotion.

Shin'ichi had striven single-mindedly and with utter sincerity to promote world peace, and his listeners could sense the depth of his feelings.

The responsive chord that sincerity strikes in people's hearts transcends all national boundaries. Sincerity is the tie that brings people together.

AFTER SHIN'ICHI finished speaking, one of the officials from Peking University delivered words of thanks.

This was then followed by remarks from a student representative, who described the Soka University students' research papers, which Shin'ichi had presented to them, as a "symbol of friendship between the people and youth of China and Japan as well as a crystallization of the warm goodwill of our Japanese friends." Stating that the Japanese people were good friends of the Chinese people and expressing the wish that future generations would continue working together to build lasting friendship, the student added: "We hope that you, President Yamamoto, and your colleagues here today will communicate this message to the Japanese people, Japanese youth and Soka University students.

"All of you have brought the friendship of the Japanese

people to the people of China. We hope that in turn you will take home with you the deep friendship of the Chinese people and youth. I would like to express our profound appreciation again for the fact that you, President Yamamoto, and your delegation have visited Peking University a second time in order to present five thousand books to our library."

Shin'ichi applauded enthusiastically and said with firm conviction: "Thank you for these noble words of friendship. I promise I will convey your feelings to the people of Japan and, in particular, the youth."

A pupil from the Peking University Allied Elementary School then said joyfully, "Please tell our little friends in Japan to visit us here in China, too."

After the book presentation ceremony, Shin'ichi and his party were shown around the Peking University

library. On the first floor, the gift of five thousand books was on display, neatly divided by subject area, including mechanics, mathematics, medicine, engineering and Japanese literature.

Treasuring books is the same as treasuring the spirit.

Mineko said to her husband: "You can see that they really value these books. I can sense their warm appreciation."

Shin'ichi nodded: "Isn't that wonderful? They've truly understood the spirit in which we made this gift."

Mutual understanding and consideration give rise to a beautiful symphony of friendship. The first step to deepening friendship is to deepen one's own consideration for others.

AFTER VISITING the Peking University library, Shin'ichi and his party sat down at a table with a dozen or so students from the university's Japanese department.

"How long have you been studying Japanese?" Shin'ichi asked.

"Eight months," replied one of the students in Japanese with excellent pronunciation.

"You're very good," Shin'ichi said. "Let's study some Japanese together, then. I'll ask questions and you reply in Japanese." The students smiled and nodded.

"Let's start by you saying the opposite of the word I give you. What's the opposite of up?"

"Down," everyone replied.

Shin'ichi went on to ask several opposites in the same way. He also asked them about the names of Japanese cities and ways of counting. It was a very relaxed and friendly "lesson," punctuated by frequent smiles and laughter.

Shin'ichi wanted to break down any psychological barriers the students might have against Japanese people. China had been invaded by the Japanese military, and many of its people had been killed. No doubt these young people had heard about this tragic history on numerous occasions from their parents and others, and as such their feelings about Japan and the Japanese must have been conflicted.

It is crucial for the Japanese to have a proper understanding of their country's past history and to sincerely apologize for those things that deserve an apology. From there, the next step is to find common ground with others as fellow human beings through bilateral exchange and positive interaction and thereby build ties of trust and friendship. The warmth produced through heart-to-heart communication and an earnest desire for friendship are the only means with which to melt the icy walls of antagonism and misunderstanding that have been forged by history. That's why exchange on the level of ordinary citizens is so important.

Shin'ichi next asked the students, "If you could go somewhere overseas while you're a student, where would you go?"

"Japan, of course," came their vigorous and immediate reply.

"Japan is the closest country to China," one of the students added. "It's our neighbor. We definitely want to go there."

Shin'ichi was very happy to hear this. "Please do visit Japan. We'll give you a warm and hearty welcome," he told them.

The students expressed their delight at this invitation.

As a sign of friendship, Shin'ichi presented them with Soka University pins and ballpoint pens.

THAT EVENING, the Peking University Student Association hosted a "Welcome Night" in the university auditorium. The event included choral performances of Japanese folk songs, a humorous dance by children wearing table tennis uniforms, a Beijing Opera aria, a sword dance and various instrumental performances. The entire university community contributed to making the evening a wonderful occasion.

Shortly after ten the following morning, December 4, Shin'ichi met with top officials of Peking University at the Beijing Hotel, where he was staying. After conveying his heartfelt appreciation for the hospitality he and his party had received over the past few days, Shin'ichi proposed developing an exchange program for faculty and students of Soka University and Peking University.

One of the Peking University officials smiled and said enthusiastically: "That's a great idea. We'd like to consider it further and do everything we can to make it a reality."

They agreed to keep in close communication and continue working to maintain their amicable ties. They also agreed to exchange research journals and academic materials on a regular basis. Academic exchange between the two institutions had been advanced one step further.

When Shin'ichi expressed his wish to donate books to Wuhan University as well, the officials smiled and nodded. One of them said: "I'm sure the university will be very glad to hear that. We'll be happy to communicate your wish to them."

Shin'ichi then presented the Peking University officials with a copy of the list of three thousand books he planned to donate to Wuhan University.

One of them remarked with deep emotion: "I can see that you are quite serious about promoting educational and cultural exchange with China. There are many individuals who talk about promoting Japan–China friendship while they're here visiting China but then do nothing to back up their words. You, however, are always taking the next step and making constant efforts to open the way forward. And you act with such speed. Your sincerity is very apparent."

There was nothing Shin'ichi disliked more than people making empty promises on which they failed to follow through. He believed that in order to accomplish anything worthwhile, it is vital to seize the moment and act quickly.

FOLLOWING HIS meeting with top officials of Peking University, Shin'ichi visited the China-Japan Friendship Association in the afternoon. There, he met with friends he had made on his first visit to China in May and June of that year, including Vice President Zhang Xiangshan, Secretary-General Sun Pinghua and council members Jin Sucheng and Lin Liyun, discussing with them ways to ensure lasting good relations between the two countries.

On October 1, in between his first China visit and this one, Shin'ichi had welcomed Sun Pinghua to the Seikyo Shimbun Building in Tokyo. At that time, Mr. Sun had been visiting Japan as a member of a Chinese friendship delegation and had flown from Beijing to Tokyo on September 29, on the very first regular flight initiated between the two cities. Shin'ichi had also been able to meet and talk with Lin Liyun on October 21, at the Soka Gakkai's Kansai Culture Center in Osaka, when she was in Japan as the leader of the Central Philharmonic Orchestra of China (now the China National Symphony Orchestra), which was then on tour.

Sun Pinghua and Lin Liyun thanked Shin'ichi for the warm welcome they had received on their respective trips to Japan, and they seemed very happy at this third opportunity to meet with him. Steady progress was being made toward building a solid history of bilateral exchange.

Vice President Zhang thought very highly of Shin'ichi's writing activities following his first visit to China, remarking: "In spite of how busy you were, you devoted tremendous energy to writing. Moreover, you told the truth about China and presented our thoughts and feelings honestly to the people of Japan. You did this, I'm certain, knowing that your writings might stir a barrage of opposition from some quarters. I deeply appreciate the sincerity and courage of your actions."

Shin'ichi replied with firm resolve: "Thank you. I am committed to promoting friendship between our countries. Just as genuine trust cannot be forged without giving oneself completely to the effort, a real path of exchange cannot be opened with empty words. Sincerity is the very soul of friendship. Just as waves only wear down a boulder by striking it again and again, let's break down the barriers to friendship between our countries by steadily working toward our shared goal."

Mahatma Gandhi declared, "My honesty is a precious treasure to me, and I can ill afford to lose it."[6] This was also Shin'ichi's heartfelt belief.

Numerous topics were discussed during their almost two-hour talk, including world affairs, various issues facing Japan, the establishment of lasting bilateral friendship and leadership principles.

SHIN'ICHI HAD A packed schedule during this China visit. It had been planned that way at his request, so that he could make the most of his short stay.

Once time passes it can never be regained. Great achievements can only be realized by continuously seizing opportunities when they present themselves and giving one's all to doing what must be done.

On the evening of December 4, Shin'ichi and his party attended a welcome banquet at the Great Hall of the People hosted by President Liao Chengzhi of the China-Japan Friendship Association. It was a pleasant occasion that expressed the sincere friendship of their Chinese hosts.

At the banquet, Shin'ichi said that during this trip, great progress had been made in furthering exchange between Soka University and Peking University. Expressing his firm resolve to work for China–Japan friendship, he added: "As a Buddhist organization striving to promote peace and culture, the Soka Gakkai has forged ahead on its chosen course to this day surmounting all manner of criticism and abuse. We will continue to work wholeheartedly to build a golden bridge of friendship between our two countries. I hope you will continue to advise and guide us in this endeavor."

Anti-Chinese forces had harshly criticized the Soka Gakkai for its earnest efforts to promote friendship between Japan and China, but Shin'ichi had been prepared for that. All that mattered to him was that he remain true to his commitment to peace and to realizing the prosperity and happiness of the people of both countries. He wanted to let his Chinese hosts know that he was determined to press resolutely forward for that purpose, unafraid of any obstacle that might arise in the process.

The following day, December 5, Shin'ichi was scheduled to meet with Chinese Vice Premier Deng Xiaoping. When he and his party arrived at the Great Hall of the People shortly after ten that morning, they were welcomed by Vice Premier Deng as well as representatives from the China-Japan Friendship Association, Peking University and others.

As Shin'ichi greeted and shook hands with the vice premier, whom he was meeting for the first time, Mr. Deng looked over toward Liao Chengzhi standing next to him and said: "I've heard about you from Mr. Liao. I think you have a message worth considering in terms of China's future. But the problems are complex."

Mr. Deng's face clouded over for a moment, then was all smiles.

THE MEETING in the Great Hall of the People began. Vice Premier Deng Xiaoping courteously thanked Shin'ichi for the donation of books to the Peking

University library. Shin'ichi and his party were deeply moved and impressed by the sincerity of the heartfelt appreciation expressed by even the vice premier for the gift to the university.

Referring to the United Nations' designation for the coming year as International Women's Year, Shin'ichi proposed a visit to Japan by Deng Yingchao, the wife of Chinese Premier Zhou Enlai, and other Chinese women and youth leaders. With the new direct air route linking Tokyo and Beijing, the journey would only take a few hours. But the distance separating Japan and China was not so much physical as it was political and emotional. Shin'ichi wished to erase that distance as quickly as possible, and he thought that women and youth could play a very important part in achieving that.

Women, like the earth, have the power to shake things up from the foundation. They also have the immense power to transform daily realities, in accord with Tolstoy's observation that "women form public opinion."[7] And youth represent the future. If young people change, the next generation will change without fail.

Deng Xiaoping smiled and nodded at Shin'ichi's suggestion. "I will pass this message along, and we will give it our consideration."

The conversation then turned to prospects for a China-Japan peace and friendship treaty. While talking about peace in Asia in that context, Shin'ichi said, "The Soviet Union is not planning to attack China." The vice premier replied, "That is a very difficult matter to judge," raising his hand up as if to stop any further discussion of the subject.

On his previous visit to China, Shin'ichi sensed that,

in the midst of the turmoil of the Cultural Revolution, a certain group of people had usurped power and were manipulating the party and state apparatus at will. He realized that even the nation's top leaders had to be very careful about what they said, as this group had informers everywhere.

Shin'ichi thought to himself: *It's possible that the vice premier is hesitant to discuss the Sino-Soviet conflict—the most critical issue facing China—out of concern that his remarks might be turned into political ammunition by his adversaries. Or, perhaps he is just extremely cautious with regard to the Soviet Union....*

SHIN'ICHI WAS glad that he had already given China-Japan Friendship Association President Liao Chengzhi a detailed report on such topics as Soviet Premier Aleksey Kosygin's message that the Soviet Union had no intention of attacking China.

Shin'ichi changed the subject. Quick responsiveness is the essence of diplomacy.

He asked Vice Premier Deng, "What do you think will be the most important and fundamental attitude for advancing friendship between our two countries from now on?"

Nodding enthusiastically, the vice premier remarked: "The peoples of China and Japan need to continuously deepen mutual understanding, friendship and interaction. We share a history of interaction that goes back more than two thousand years. In all that time, relations between our two countries have been in an objectionable state for only about one hundred years. We were subjugated by Japanese militarism, which brought immense suffering not only on the Chinese people but on the Japanese people as well. For this, we do not blame the people of Japan.

"But that is in the past, and diplomatic relations between our countries have been normalized. What we need to do now is to look toward the future and strive to strengthen our ties for generations to come."

As the Chinese educator Tao Xingzhi (1891–1946) has said, "A golden age lies ahead, it lies in the future."[8]

Shin'ichi next asked about the health of Chairman Mao Zedong and Premier Zhou Enlai. Vice Premier Deng spoke about the premier's condition in particular: "Premier Zhou has been hospitalized for the past six months, and his condition is worse than we expected. His workload had been growing for the last several years, and he became worn out. We are doing all we can to lessen the burden on him as much as possible. Now, we only report to him on the most critical matters, and we only ask him for instructions on days when his physical condition is good.

"Premier Zhou very much wishes to meet with you. However, at this time, we are not allowing him to see anyone, no matter who it might be."

Shin'ichi responded: "I understand. If you have the opportunity, please convey my best wishes to Premier Zhou, and tell him I am sincerely praying for his health. And please also give my best to Vice Premier Li Xiannian, whom I met on my last visit."

SHIN'ICHI ALSO pointedly asked Vice Premier Deng Xiaoping when the next National People's

Congress, China's governing body, would be convened.

In the past, plenary sessions of the National People's Congress had been held annually; however, the last such session was convened from late December 1964 to early January 1965, and none had been held since the start of the Cultural Revolution. Shin'ichi was deeply concerned that if this situation continued, China would lose credibility as a nation.

Vice Premier Deng replied, "I think the National People's Congress will be convened soon."

Shin'ichi had ventured to ask the question because he believed that if a date were officially announced, governments around the globe would regard China as a state that intended to function based on the rule of law and would feel more secure. Shin'ichi had given serious thought to how China could gain trust and understanding in the world.

At the news conference following the meeting, Shin'ichi shared the vice premier's statement regarding the convening of the National People's Congress. On December 6, the next day, many of the major newspapers in Japan ran such headlines as "China's National People's Congress Set to Convene."

True friendship is embodied in the sincerity and commitment of one's empathy for others.

Additionally, Shin'ichi had also proposed to the vice premier that Japan and China work together on archeological and other research on the ancient Silk Road trade routes. He made this suggestion because he believed that it would help the two countries reaffirm their profound historical ties as well as further scholarly exchange. Shin'ichi forthrightly offered the vice premier specific proposals aimed at realizing his wish to deepen bilateral friendship.

No doubt Vice Premier Deng could feel Shin'ichi's profound concern for China. At the end of the nearly hour-long encounter, Vice Premier Deng said: "I hope you'll come to visit China whenever you have the time. We will always heartily welcome you as our friend."

The Swiss philosopher Carl Hilty (1833–1909) once wrote, "My ideal is to become a useful friend to many."[9] This was also Shin'ichi's strong wish.

FOLLOWING THE meeting with Vice Premier Deng, Shin'ichi and his party toured Tiantan Park. It is the site of the Temple of Heaven complex, where the emperors of the past conducted ceremonies in worship of the heavenly gods said to rule the universe. In modern times, the complex was opened to the public as a park.

Shin'ichi cheerfully greeted the people he encountered in the park, and even the little children responded warmly. He wanted to build bridges of friendship in their young hearts, too. He posed for a group photograph with about forty people at the Altar of Heaven, a three-tiered circular platform made of marble. Shin'ichi always tried to spend every free moment reaching out to people.

True philosophy, wisdom and justice are found among the ordinary people. The wisdom of the people has the power to create a bright future. The solidarity of ordinary people serves as a citadel for building peace—this was Shin'ichi's firm belief.

Shortly before seven in the evening on December 5, their last evening in China, Shin'ichi and Mineko spon-

sored a thank-you banquet for their Chinese hosts and friends at the Beijing International Club. They invited members of the China-Japan Friendship Association, representatives of Peking University, journalists and staff members of the Beijing Hotel, where they had lodged.

At the banquet, Shin'ichi gave a toast in which he expressed his heartfelt gratitude to his hosts and described the days of his current visit to China as the starting point of fostering enduring exchange between Soka University and Peking University. Noting that the travel time between the two countries had been dramatically shortened by the new direct flights, he asserted: "Now the time has come for us to shrink the emotional and spiritual distance separating us. While it is helpful to reduce the physical distance between us, it's even more important to reduce the distance between the hearts of our peoples—

in other words, to increase mutual feelings of amity based on a spirit of sincerity and abiding trust.

"No matter how close we may be in proximity," he said, "without a spirit of mutual respect and equality, the effort to build bridges of peace and friendship would just be an illusion."

Shin'ichi then emphasized that, to ensure the future of amicable bilateral relations, it would be essential to forge lasting ties of friendship on various levels among the people of both countries and promote academic and cultural exchange based on a long-term perspective.

THE THANK-YOU banquet became an occasion for friendly conversation. Shin'ichi and Mineko walked from table to table, greeting each of their guests and expressing thanks and appreciation. Shin'ichi always began by addressing each individual by name and thanking them graciously for their specific acts of kindness, support and consideration. To one, he said: "I'll never forget your heartfelt expression of friendship during the book presentation ceremony. Your words filled me with courage." To another, he said: "I know how hard you are working behind the scenes. Your efforts have been essential in making this visit a success."

Shin'ichi not only distinctly remembered each person's name and face but also his interactions with them and the efforts they had made. Perfunctory greetings can only lead to artificial, formal relations. In order to enjoy genuine interaction with others, we should strive to understand them as best we can and speak from our hearts.

As the banquet was approaching its end, China-Japan

Friendship Association President Liao Chengzhi was called out of the room to take a telephone call. When he returned, he said to Shin'ichi in a low voice: "Premier Zhou is waiting to see you."

It was a sudden request. Having heard during his meeting with Vice Premier Deng Xiaoping that the premier's health was worse than originally thought, Shin'ichi politely indicated that he did not expect to meet the statesman. "No, no, I don't want to endanger his health or impose," he said to President Liao. "I do hope you will tell him I am deeply grateful for his generosity."

President Liao looked disturbed. "Premier Zhou has strongly expressed his wish to meet you. He seems determined to do so, no matter what."

It appeared that refusing the invitation would be out of the question. Shin'ichi responded: "All right. I'll be very glad to pay my respects. But please allow me to leave right after I've done so. I don't want to place any burden on Premier Zhou in his fragile state of health."

In truth, the Chinese leader was in no condition to receive visitors. And all of the members of his medical team were opposed to his meeting with Shin'ichi.

THE PHYSICIANS caring for Premier Zhou warned him that if he insisted on meeting Shin'ichi, it could put his life in jeopardy, but the premier resolutely replied, "I must meet with President Yamamoto, regardless of the circumstances." No doubt he felt compelled to do so, and his physicians were at a loss. They spoke to the premier's wife, Madame Deng Yingchao, in an effort to convince her to dissuade the premier, but she said,

"If Comrade Enlai is so insistent on meeting President Yamamoto, then please allow him to go ahead with it." Madame Deng had comprehended her husband's deep-seated wish to meet with Shin'ichi.

Before leaving the Beijing Hotel, Shin'ichi said to President Liao: "From my group, only my wife and I will join the premier for the discussion. If he has to speak with a large group, it's certain to be tiring for him." Shin'ichi felt this was the least he could do to lessen the strain on the statesman.

The group went out of the hotel into the cold night air. It seemed to be below freezing, and the chill pierced their skin like needles. Dividing up into several cars, Shin'ichi and his party rode through the dark streets at considerable speed. After about fifteen minutes, they pulled up in front of a building, Beijing's Hospital 305, where the premier was staying. Getting out of the cars and stepping inside, they were greeted by Premier Zhou, who stood before them in a Mao suit. Extending his right arm, Shin'ichi said, "I am so grateful to have this opportunity to meet you during your convalescence."

The premier smiled and clasped his hand. "Thank you for coming."

Shin'ichi extended his left hand to gently support the premier's right forearm. In 1939, in the midst of the revolutionary struggle, Premier Zhou had fallen from a horse and broken his right arm just above the elbow. Shin'ichi was aware that his arm remained slightly twisted because of that injury.

Premier Zhou's hands were pale, resembling the hands of Josei Toda when he had grown frail in his final years.

This moved Shin'ichi deeply. The two men looked intently at each other. Shin'ichi sensed a tremendous power emanating from the premier's thin form.

It was 9:55 PM, December 5.

PREMIER ZHOU ENLAI addressed Shin'ichi in a friendly manner: "First, let's take a commemorative photograph with everyone." The premier then greeted and shook hands with each member of Shin'ichi's party. They all posed for the photograph wearing tense expressions, reflecting the significance of the occasion. After the picture was taken, Premier Zhou asked Shin'ichi to follow him. And, as previously arranged, Shin'ichi and Mineko met with the premier in a separate room, leaving the rest of the party behind.

Once they sat down, the premier calmly remarked: "President Yamamoto, I believe this is your second trip to China. On your previous visit, my health was at its worst, and I was not able to see you. But since I am now slowly recovering, I very much wanted to meet you. I'm so happy to have this opportunity."

Premier Zhou was seventy-six, and Shin'ichi was forty-six. Perhaps the premier was counting on Shin'ichi's youthful potential. As the German literary giant Johann Wolfgang von Goethe (1749–1832) wrote, "One must be young to do great things."[10] The future is created through the fresh power of youth, which is why it is so important to dedicate all one's energies to fostering young people.

Interpretation at the meeting was provided by China-Japan Friendship Association council member Lin Liyun. Mineko began to furiously scribble notes of the exchange between Premier Zhou and her husband. She was certain it would be a historic occasion, but there were no reporters present. Feeling a pressing sense of responsibility, she wrote as quickly and precisely as possible.

Premier Zhou highly valued Shin'ichi's consistent efforts to strengthen Sino–Japanese friendship. He said: "President Yamamoto, you have emphasized the need to foster amicable relations between the people of our two nations, regardless of the difficulties involved. I am extremely pleased by this. Bilateral friendship is our mutual wish. Let's strive for this together." Though he spoke in soft tones, his voice conveyed an underlying strength.

In these words, Shin'ichi felt the premier's ardent hope that a path toward lasting friendship between Japan and China could be opened. Shin'ichi also sensed that he was being entrusted to carry on the task of creating peace.

PREMIER ZHOU commented that the advances in Sino–Japanese friendship came about through the efforts of both himself and Shin'ichi. Premier Zhou's eyes sparkled as he spoke. "For the sake of the future, I hope that a peace and friendship treaty between our two countries can be signed as quickly as possible."

Calling attention to events earlier in the day, the premier mentioned: "I understand you met with Vice Premier Deng this morning. I was told of your comments by him and others concerned. I assume there's no need, then, for me to say much about the issues you discussed on that occasion." It was apparent that the premier had been informed in detail of Shin'ichi's statements regarding the Soviet Union and other matters.

"No, there's no need at all. And I don't wish to compromise your recovery, so let me say my farewells now," said Shin'ichi. But the premier shook his head slowly to indicate that Shin'ichi shouldn't rush off. Gazing at Shin'ichi and Mineko, he asked each where they had been raised.

"We are both from Tokyo," replied Shin'ichi. "Native Tokyoites are generally thought to be straightforward and simple in temperament. We're not clever. In fact, the two of us together just barely add up to one normal person." It was a humorous response. Shin'ichi wanted to make the premier feel at ease as much as possible. Such consideration is an expression of true sincerity.

Premier Zhou laughed out loud for the first time during their meeting. A moment later, his eyes narrowed as if he were looking off into the distance, and he said in a nostalgic tone, "More than fifty years ago, I left Japan when the cherry blossoms were in bloom."

Nodding, Shin'ichi said: "I see. Please come visit Japan again when it is cherry blossom season."

"I would like that very much," Premier Zhou remarked with a wistful smile. "But I'm afraid that is impossible." It pained Shin'ichi to hear this.

At that instant, a note was passed to Lin Liyun, who was interpreting. Shin'ichi had no way of knowing it then, but it was a message from the Chinese statesman's physicians telling him it was time to rest. She passed the note to the premier, but he appeared to know what it said and, without even looking at it, continued talking. Premier Zhou seemed to firmly believe that he must now spend time with and talk to Shin'ichi, even if it shortened his life.

OUT OF HIS wish not to unnecessarily tire Premier Zhou Enlai, Shin'ichi avoided initiating any conversation. He looked several times at China-Japan Friendship Association President Liao Chengzhi, who was there at the meeting, asking silently if they should bring the occasion to an end now, but each time President Liao indicated that they should continue. Finally, Shin'ichi decided to express his thoughts: "We need you to remain healthy for many years to come, Premier Zhou. China is a pivotal nation in achieving world peace. For the sake of your nation and its eight hundred million people...."

The premier seemed to rally all his strength and began to speak: "You have called China pivotal, but we have no intention to become a superpower. And China today is not economically wealthy. Nevertheless, we will make our contribution to the world. The last twenty-five years of the twentieth century will be a crucial period for all of humanity. It will be necessary for the peoples of the world to cooperate and help one another as equal partners."

"I think that is absolutely true," echoed Shin'ichi. He felt as if he were listening to the premier's final will.

The discussion had gone on for nearly thirty minutes. Shin'ichi wished he could have continued speaking with Premier Zhou forever, but he simply couldn't allow their meeting to last any longer. "I promise that I will make your opinion known to the appropriate people in Japan," he said. "And I wish to deeply thank you for taking the time to meet with me."

Shin'ichi presented Premier Zhou with a Japanese painting of bush clover and an ox-drawn court carriage, a traditional motif. He later learned that, that same evening, the premier took down a painting that had been hanging in his room and replaced it with Shin'ichi's gift.

One of the Chinese classics states: "But when two people are at one in their inmost hearts, / They shatter even the strength of iron or of bronze."[11] Strong friendship has the power to cut through even the toughest metal.

This encounter was the one and only time that Shin'ichi and Premier Zhou would ever meet. However, their friendship formed an eternal pledge and ties of trust. Shin'ichi's heart was thoroughly infused with the premier's spirit.

A NEW PAGE in the golden history of Sino–Japanese friendship had been inscribed through Shin'ichi's second trip to China.

Shin'ichi arrived back in Japan on the afternoon of December 6. Following his return, he monitored developments between China and the Soviet Union, sincerely praying and hoping for their reconciliation. He was staunchly determined to do everything possible from his own position to contribute to improving relations between the two countries, regardless of the circumstances. Unfortunately, contrary to Shin'ichi's hopes, it appeared that Sino–Soviet relations had taken a turn for the worse.

In January 1975, China convened the Fourth National People's Congress and revised its constitution. In the preamble to the new constitution, a passage stated that China would "oppose the imperialist and social-imperialist policies of aggression and war and oppose the hegemonism of the superpowers."[12]

Social-imperialism was a term that China had recently taken to employing with regard to the Soviet Union. Chinese constitutions up to then had lauded Sino–Soviet friendship, but now a clearly anti-Soviet line was being articulated. This was the period when China was dominated by the Gang of Four. Perhaps Premier Kosygin's message had not reached their ears. The Soviet Union responded by harshly criticizing China, and it seemed that relations were sure to deteriorate even further.

At the congress, an ill Premier Zhou presented a report on governmental activities and proposed the "Four Modernizations," a plan aimed at "[accomplishing] the comprehensive modernization of agriculture, industry, national defense and science and technology before the end of the century, so that our national economy will be advancing in the front ranks of the world."[13] The far-reaching policies of the Four Modernizations provided the groundwork for the paths of openness and reform that China subsequently followed, leading to the nation's immense development that is evident today.

Dr. Kong Fanfeng, the director of the Zhou Enlai Research Center of China's Nankai University, later wrote about the background against which Premier Zhou could propose those policies. Dr. Kong pointed out that a sound and accurate perception of the international situation was indispensable for launching the Four Modernizations. He also indicated that by learning of the Soviet position through President Yamamoto, Premier Zhou strengthened his conviction that war would not break out between China and the Soviet Union, and was thus able to go ahead and boldly implement his plans for modernizing China.

SHIN'ICHI FIRMLY pledged to himself: "It is essential that the antagonism between China and the Soviet Union be transformed into friendship. No matter how dim the prospects seem, I will never give up this struggle. It can only be achieved by persevering in dialogue."

In April 1975, just three months after China proclaimed its anti-Soviet stance in the preamble of its new constitution, Shin'ichi made his third visit to the country, at which time he again met and talked with Vice Premier Deng Xiaoping. Their conversations focused on Sino–Soviet relations. Mr. Deng expressed an increasing distrust of the Soviet Union. He asserted that if any country were to start a third world war it would probably be the United States or the Soviet Union, indicating that he regarded the Soviet Union in particular as the greater threat. With the Gang of Four still at the height of their power, it is possible Vice Premier Deng felt obligated to voice these strongly anti-Soviet views. Looking back on the history of Sino–Soviet relations, the vice premier spoke openly of China's distrust of its northern neighbor.

Shin'ichi said: "Vice Premier Deng, if the same tension and antagonism persists between China and the Soviet Union for the upcoming decades, centuries and millennia, it will create insecurity for the people of both nations and the entire world. Do you have any desire to make some gesture of friendship, to take the initiative in opening the way to global peace? For the sake of the world, do you have any intention to hold a conference with Soviet representatives?"

But the vice premier only criticized the Soviet Union, saying that representatives of the two nations had met on numerous occasions to discuss their border disputes, to no avail. Shin'ichi said, "The reality of the situation may be challenging, but if the Soviet Union were to take a step in changing its basic attitude toward China, wouldn't you be interested in trying to improve relations?"

Vice Premier Deng replied: "That would depend on the attitude of the Soviet leadership. Our feelings for the Soviet people have always been amicable."

Shin'ichi thought to himself: *It's clear that China really would like to coexist peacefully with the Soviet Union. And the Soviet Union wishes the same thing. No matter how complicated the situation, there is nothing fundamental blocking the improvement of bilateral relations. I will give my all to pursuing further dialogue with Chinese and Soviet leaders.*

The month after his third trip to China, Shin'ichi again visited the Soviet Union, where he met and spoke with Premier Aleksey Kosygin and other top Soviet leaders.

The courage to triumph over despair and hopelessness is the force for creating a better future.

IN APRIL 1975, six government-financed exchange students from China were welcomed to the campus of Soka University. They were the first Chinese students to formally study in Japan since the establishment of the People's Republic of China. Shin'ichi served as personal guarantor for each of them. On November 2 of the same year, in line with a proposal made by Shin'ichi, these exchange students, along with representative faculty members and students at Soka University, planted the Zhou Cherry Tree on campus as an expression of their prayers for the health of Premier Zhou Enlai and as a symbol of the wish for lasting peace between China and Japan.

In the following year, however, Premier Zhou and then Chairman Mao Zedong passed away. Hua Guofeng became the new chairman, but relations between China and the Soviet Union remained frigid. Furthermore, in 1979, one year before the Sino-Soviet Treaty of Friendship, Alliance and Mutual Assistance was set to expire, China announced its intention to terminate the pact. Moreover, in response to the Soviet invasion of Afghanistan at the end of that year, China informed its neighbor that it would indefinitely suspend talks aimed at improving bilateral relations.

When Shin'ichi visited China for the fifth time in April 1980, many in China were harshly critical of the Soviet invasion of Afghanistan. Some Chinese officials with whom he spoke asked him to refrain from traveling to the Soviet Union as much as possible so as not to jeopardize his efforts to strengthen Sino–Japanese friendship.

In response, Shin'ichi stated: "I understand your feelings. However, the times are rapidly changing. With the approach of the twenty-first century, it is essential that we somehow redirect the course of humanity toward peace. The time has passed when the great powers can fight and hate one another. I believe that we now need a humanistic approach that seeks to create harmony while finding the good in others and fosters a new age by encouraging people to help one another."

Shin'ichi made his case with all sincerity, but he had difficulty convincing his Chinese friends. To them, it always came down to which was more important to him, China or the Soviet Union.

The path of following one's principles is always blocked by daunting obstacles. A new path can only be opened up by overcoming those impediments.

SHIN'ICHI SPOKE to his Chinese friends honestly and sincerely: "I love China. It is precious to me. At the same time, I love all people. All of humanity is precious. Soviet leaders have clearly told me that they have no intention to attack China, and I have communicated that message to your nation's leaders. I want China and the Soviet Union to be friends. I am sure that you will one day understand my thoughts on this matter."

Regardless of how difficult the circumstances might become, Shin'ichi refused to give up. As the Chinese writer Ba Jin (1904–2005) once wrote: "I am a person who cannot be beaten. I am a person who cannot despair."[14] Shin'ichi had met with Ba Jin on several occasions and engaged in dialogue with the writer. Ba Jin's words resonated with Shin'ichi's attitude toward life.

Winning means to stay true to one's convictions, no matter what happens. Shin'ichi continued to carry out dialogue with the confidence that all people wish for peace, guided by his belief that everyone has the Buddha nature within.

On his fifth trip to China, in 1980, he met Chinese Communist Party Chairman Hua Guofeng and asked about the direction China would be taking in the future. Then in 1981, he made his third trip to the Soviet Union, where he met with Soviet Premier Nikolai Tikhonov (1905–97).

Shin'ichi pressed ahead out of an earnest desire to open the way to peace for all humanity.

In March 1982, Soviet Communist Party General Secretary Leonid Brezhnev called for the improvement of Sino–Soviet bilateral relations. The times began to change. Some six months later, Chinese Communist Party Chairman Hu Yaobang (1915–89) stipulated that relations could be improved if three outstanding obstacles could be resolved—the Soviet invasion of Afghanistan, the deployment of Soviet forces along the Chinese border and Soviet support for the Vietnamese invasion of Cambodia.

In his inaugural speech as general secretary of the Soviet Communist Party in March 1985, Mikhail Gorbachev expressed his hope that Sino–Soviet relations could be improved. Following that, the two nations agreed to reopen discussions on their border dispute, and a foreign ministerial conference was held in Moscow in 1988. And in May 1989, Mr. Gorbachev traveled to China, becoming the first top Soviet leader to visit the country in thirty years. While there, he conferred with Deng Xiaoping—chairman of the Central Military Commission and China's de facto ruler—and the two leaders announced that bilateral relations had finally been normalized.

That summit meeting marked the dawn of a new era of transformation in which the world would move away from the Cold War toward a period of relaxing tensions.

IN 1990, CHINESE Premier Li Peng visited the Soviet Union. In 1991, Chinese Communist Party Central Committee General Secretary Jiang Zemin went to the Soviet Union, where the foreign ministers of both nations signed a treaty resolving disputes along the eastern section of the Sino–Soviet border.

Shin'ichi was overjoyed to see the steady advance of improving relations between China and the Soviet Union. He had prayed steadfastly for the realization of the peaceful coexistence of the two nations. As a private individual, he had striven tirelessly in that direction and consistently urged the leaders of each country to cultivate peace and friendship with their neighbor. Though his efforts may have only stirred a small ripple, Shin'ichi's desire to see China and the Soviet Union achieve harmony had become a reality.

Watching a television broadcast of the amicable

exchange between Mikhail Gorbachev and Deng Xiao-ping during the former's visit to China in May 1989, Shin'ichi said to Mineko: "This is wonderful. Perhaps Vice Premier Deng took my plea to heart. The curtain is rising on a new age, in which mistrust will be replaced by trust."

"Yes," Mineko responded. "Watching this is like a dream come true, isn't it?"

"Kosen-rufu is the realization of the happiness of humanity and peace in the world. As a Buddhist, I will continue to work wholeheartedly to achieve that. It doesn't matter to me whether people notice, or what society thinks. History will be the judge, eventually. I'm the second-generation disciple of Soka Gakkai founder Tsunesaburo Makiguchi, who fought against the oppression of the Japanese military government and died for his beliefs. I'm the disciple of second Soka Gakkai president Josei Toda, who upheld the philosophy of global citizenship and made his famous declaration for the abolition of nuclear weapons. As such, there is no way that I will ever cease my struggle for peace, no matter what the circumstances. That is my iron-clad conviction."

The Russian diplomat, Yuri Kuznetsov, a former counselor at the Soviet Embassy in Tokyo at the time when Shin'ichi made his first trip to the Soviet Union, later reflected on Shin'ichi's visits to China and the Soviet Union and his discussions with leaders of those nations: "There is no denying the contribution he made to the normalization of relations between China and the Soviet Union. I believe that without his efforts for the normalization of relations at that time, the broad-ranging ties that exist between China and Russia today would not have been possible."

It is difficult to detect the currents flowing beneath the surface. However, Shin'ichi firmly believed that actions based on noble convictions shape the undercurrents that transform the course of history.

THE JAPANESE writer and statesman Yukio Ozaki (pen name: Gakudo Ozaki, 1859–1954) was a significant contributor to the establishment of Japan's parliamentary system of government. He once wrote: "Today's world can be saved through human wisdom, not by brute force or violence. That is the power inherent in the wisdom of people who sincerely wish for the happiness of humanity and world peace."[15] Kosen-rufu is the creation of a peace that embodies that wisdom.

The curtain rose on 1975, which the Soka Gakkai had designated as "The Year of Education and the Family."

On New Year's Day, Shin'ichi attended a New Year's meeting held at the Mentor-Disciple Hall on the third floor of the Soka Gakkai Headquarters building in Shinano-machi, Tokyo. Shin'ichi began the year in high spirits, pledging to the Gohonzon to completely dedicate himself again to kosen-rufu and world peace in 1975. Shortly thereafter, on January 6, he flew to the United States.

It was apparent that among the American public, some people were both impressed and puzzled by Shin'ichi, who was visiting the United States following trips to China and the Soviet Union, two countries that remained antagonistic toward each other. The American newsmagazine *Time* published an article about him and the Soka Gakkai in its January 13, 1975, edition under the somewhat sarcastic headline "The Super Missionary."[16] The article reported on the Soka Gakkai's organizational development since Shin'ichi had become its president, mentioning the *Seikyo Shimbun*, Soka University and other institutions. It also related that Shin'ichi had previously met with Soviet Premier Aleksey Kosygin and then Chinese Premier Zhou Enlai, and that on his current U.S. trip he would be meeting with U.N. Secretary-General Kurt Waldheim (1918–2007). Touching on Shin'ichi's proposals for complete international nuclear disarmament and the formation of a world food bank, the article stated, "His most consuming passion is the creation of an international people-to-people crusade against war." Yet at the same time, the article implied that Shin'ichi's actions and proposals were simply a means for the Soka Gakkai to obtain political power. This indicated a lack of real understanding of Shin'ichi's commitment to peace.

Shin'ichi arrived in Los Angeles shortly after half past six in the evening local time on January 6. After participating in several events there, he arrived in New York on the evening of January 8. The following day, he met and spoke with the literary critic Shuichi Kato, a visiting Japanese professor at Yale University. Shin'ichi had developed a deep friendship with Professor Kato through their numerous encounters in Japan. During their talks, they freely discussed the role that Japan could play for the sake of humanity's future as part of a relationship with the United States and the Soviet Union.

ON JANUARY 9, Shin'ichi made an official visit to Columbia University in New York. Columbia was founded in 1754, making it the fifth university to be established in the United States. Past students of the highly prestigious institution include twenty-sixth U.S. president Theodore Roosevelt and thirty-second U.S. president Franklin Roosevelt. Numerous Nobel laureates also hailed from Columbia, and Hideki Yukawa—the first Japanese to be awarded a Nobel Prize—served as a visiting professor at the school.

When Shin'ichi and his party arrived at Columbia, the university president was away on business, but they were welcomed by thirteen faculty members, with three vice presidents among them. They enjoyed a lively discussion, and Shin'ichi spoke of his ideas on various topics, such as forming a "United Nations of Education," an "International Conference of University Rectors" and a

"World Students Conference." He earnestly sought to open a dialogue for bringing the world together through educational exchange.

Great things are achieved through the steady accumulation of many inconspicuous small actions.

The following morning, January 10, Shin'ichi visited the United Nations Headquarters and met and talked with Secretary-General Kurt Waldheim in his offices on the thirty-eighth floor. Mr. Waldheim was fifty-six and had been born in Austria. He had a strong interest in the Soka Gakkai's Buddhist movement that at that point extended to dozens of countries worldwide. This was Shin'ichi's third visit to the United Nations Headquarters, following visits in 1960 and 1967.

Greeting Shin'ichi with a firm handshake, Secretary-General Waldheim took a seat, the U.N. logo adorning the wall behind him. Smiling and speaking politely, he said he had read many of Shin'ichi's writings and knew how earnestly his guest was working for peace. The secretary-general also commented that he would like to further familiarize himself with and examine the principles upheld by the Soka Gakkai and see them reflected in the operation of the United Nations as an essential organization for peace.

Shin'ichi was deeply gratified and humbled by the secretary-general's statement. He had thought long and hard about how to overcome such problems as the nuclear threat and world hunger, and had made several proposals for solving these issues on a fundamental level. It appeared that the U.N. secretary-general, who shouldered a weighty responsibility for the future of all humanity, had taken note of Shin'ichi's philosophy and proposals and held them in high regard.

The world was seeking the wisdom of Buddhism.

SHIN'ICHI HAD several questions prepared for Secretary-General Waldheim, and their meeting was conducted as a sort of question-and-answer session. Shin'ichi began by broaching the issue of the elimination of nuclear weapons: "At present, the number of nations that possess nuclear weapons is increasing. I'd like to know what you think about this. Also, I wish to ask if you have a candid message for the people of Japan, the only country to have suffered nuclear attack."

As Shin'ichi asked this question, the stirring words of second Soka Gakkai president Josei Toda's Declaration for the Abolition of Nuclear Weapons—which he made on September 8, 1957, at Mitsuzawa Stadium in Yokohama, Kanagawa Prefecture—reverberated in his heart: "We, the citizens of the world, have an inviolable right to live.... Even if a country should conquer the world through the use of nuclear weapons, the conquerors must be viewed as devils, as evil incarnate. I believe that it is the mission of every member of the youth division in Japan to disseminate this idea throughout the globe."

As Mr. Toda's disciple, Shin'ichi sought to convey his mentor's ideals to the world by writing voluminously, speaking exhaustively and traveling the globe to engage top leaders and thinkers in dialogue. The role of the disciple is to realize the mentor's vision, and that is the path of the shared commitment of mentor and disciple in the Soka Gakkai. When the mentor's spirit is passed on to disciples and expands into a broad movement, the great wish for kosen-rufu is actualized.

Secretary-General Waldheim spoke softly but with conviction: "We must at all costs avoid a nuclear war. I can well understand why Japan, as the only nation to have suffered nuclear attack, has such a strong interest in nuclear weapons issues. The United Nations should be working on reexamining the Nuclear Non-Proliferation Treaty, and I would like to initiate a conference for that purpose."

It was a concise response that was straight to the point.

Shin'ichi posed his next question: "There is a very real possibility that conflict will erupt again in the Middle East. What are your thoughts on this matter?"

Since its establishment, the state of Israel had been locked in a bitter conflict with the Arab nations, and on four occasions the conflict spilled over into open war. In October 1973, the Yom Kippur War—also known as the Fourth Arab-Israeli War—broke out when the joint forces of Egypt and Syria attacked Israel. Though that war came to a rapid conclusion, the situation was such that yet another outbreak could occur at any moment.

SHIN'ICHI EARNESTLY hoped for peace to be realized in the Middle East. When fighting erupted there, his heart ached and he chanted for the happiness and peace of the people there.

In response to Shin'ichi's query, Secretary-General Waldheim said: "Because of the rapprochement that is taking place between the superpowers, I don't believe this will lead directly to a world war. However, problems in one area always tend to spread. The United Nations hopes to resolve this issue through a multi-step process of peace negotiations, but if these talks bear no fruit by this spring, the mandate allowing U.N. troops to remain in the region will expire. I am in fact worried that that will be the case. To establish peace in the region, one important focus is the withdrawal of Israeli troops from the Sinai Peninsula. With the cooperation of U.S. Secretary of State Henry Kissinger, I hope that through dialogue we can fulfill the conditions for resolving these issues."

Shin'ichi also asked about the ongoing dispute on the Mediterranean island of Cyprus between Turkish Cypriots and Greek Cypriots, the problem of food shortages in countries that suffer from famine and the fighting still raging in Indochina.

Speaking forthrightly on the topic of the United Nation's function in the world, Shin'ichi said: "UNESCO (United Nations Educational, Scientific and Cultural Organization) and various countries are advocating the role of the United Nations, and I feel that the United Nation's activities are becoming increasingly essential with regard to global peace and human prosperity. Unfortunately, I think the world's awareness of and interest in the organization is insufficient. There is an urgent need to promote understanding of the United Nation's role. I have numerous friends around the globe, and Soka Gakkai members also live in many different countries. With the cooperation of all these people, I believe the time would be right for creating a global solidarity of ordinary citizens committed to supporting the United Nations."

Shin'ichi was deeply convinced that humanity must give up the folly of war and learn to live in cooperation as members of the same global family. Toward that end, people must transcend the limitations of nationality, ethnicity, religion and other distinctions so that they may unite as global citizens and, centering on the United Nations, work for lasting peace. This was his determination.

SHIN'ICHI WENT on to explain why he thought a global solidarity of ordinary citizens committed to supporting the United Nations was necessary.

"The United Nations has a very significant role to play in the twenty-first century, and it is crucial that it doesn't lose credibility or become dominated by the self-centered interests of the larger countries. That is why I wish to state that, rather than relying solely on nation-states, the United Nations should gain support among ordinary citizens who believe in the organization. What do you think about this? I am prepared to contribute whatever I can to such an effort."

His eyes shining with enthusiasm, Secretary-General Waldheim replied: "In order to make the public properly informed about the United Nation's goals, we certainly do need, just as you say, the active support of citizens around the globe. And I deeply appreciate the efforts you have made so far on this matter. We need people all around the world to work together in support of the United Nations. I am especially concerned about the recent trend—evident even within the United Nations— for national egos to take priority over any consideration for the welfare and peace of humanity as a whole. I place all my hopes in the contributions of ordinary citizens such as you, President Yamamoto."

This reflected the United Nations' high expectations for the Soka Gakkai, which was working for the good of all humanity.

"I understand," said Shin'ichi. "We'll do our best to live up to your expectations. Given the limited time we have for today's meeting, I have taken the liberty of bringing along several written proposals I would like to present to the United Nations concerning such topics as the eradication of nuclear weapons, the problems of hunger and overpopulation, and prospects for a United Nations University. I hope you will have an opportunity to read through them later."

And so saying, Shin'ichi handed the documents to the secretary-general.

"There's one more question I'd like to ask," Shin'ichi said. "What do you think is the major obstruction to world peace?"

Without a moment's hesitation, the secretary-general replied, "Lack of trust."

Nodding vigorously, Shin'ichi leaned forward and declared: "I completely agree. I believe the essential key to achieving peace is to overcome the suspicion that has taken root in people's hearts and change that mistrust into trust."

SHIN'ICHI'S VOICE grew more impassioned: "I believe that the path for transforming mistrust into trust is dialogue, as well as cultural exchange and personal interaction. I pledge to continue to do everything I can as a private citizen to open the way for dialogue and exchange."

Shin'ichi then handed U.N. Secretary-General Kurt Waldheim three bound volumes.

"These volumes contain signatures to a petition calling for the eradication of war and nuclear armaments," he explained. "The Soka Gakkai youth division conducted a petition drive and gathered the signatures of more than ten million people in Japan. This is just one portion of them. The eradication of nuclear weapons is a cause that the Soka Gakkai takes to heart. It is also the heartfelt cry of the Japanese people. I hope you will consider these signatures as an expression of the deep wish of the youth of Japan, and that the United Nations will stir an even greater groundswell for the elimination of all nuclear armaments."

The secretary-general accepted the bound petitions and opened the pages. He then held aloft the volumes in a gesture of respectful acceptance and declared: "These are extremely precious. I have the highest regard for your activities. I am deeply moved."

Shin'ichi personally delivered the signatures to the U.N. secretary-general out of his ardent desire to reply to the young people who had worked so hard for peace.

The initial inspiration for the petition drive was born when, at the 35th Soka Gakkai Headquarters General Meeting in November 1972, Shin'ichi entrusted the youth division with the task of spearheading a movement aimed at protecting the universal right of all people to live. In February of the following year, the young men's division adopted the "Youth Appeal to Protect the Right to Live" during its general meeting. One of the points made in the appeal was a call for "the elimination of nuclear weapons and all military armaments and the abolition of war." The young men's division subsequently decided to launch a petition drive to help realize this objective. And in March, the young women's and student divisions each held general meetings at which they resolved to begin full-fledged activities for peace.

These developments attest to the joint struggle for peace waged by mentor and disciples, and furthermore signify the expansion, from mentor to disciples, of an enduring current of peace.

BASED ON THE "Youth Appeal to Protect the Right to Live," Soka Gakkai youth divisions in regions across Japan established committees to organize petition drives in support of the abolition of nuclear weapons. In the summer of 1973, youth division volunteers took to the streets in communities such as Hiroshima, Nagasaki and Okinawa in order to collect signatures. And on September 8—the anniversary of Josei Toda's Declaration for the Abolition of Nuclear Weapons—a young men's division leaders meeting was held in Yokohama, Kanagawa Prefecture, during which plans for the petition drive were further solidified, leading to its development into a nationwide campaign.

In January 1974, the youth division settled on a goal of collecting ten million signatures by the end of the year, with the bulk of their effort being made in the months of July and August.

When young people take action with diligence and determination, their efforts will without doubt have a tremendous impact on society. Youth have the power to change the world.

Youth division members stood under the blazing summer sun at train stations and other public spaces, calling out for nuclear abolition with hoarse voices, entreating citizens to sign the petition.

One day, Shin'ichi and Mineko were driving through a busy shopping district in Tokyo when they saw a group of youth division members collecting signatures under the hot sun. Asking the driver to stop the car, Shin'ichi watched the young people. Though they were enthusiastically calling out to passersby, the reactions they received were mixed. Some gladly signed the petition and spoke kindly to the young people. But most of those walking along the streets showed no interest, and some even frowned or sneered at them. No matter how people reacted, the youth division members kept smiling and speaking out emphatically against the threat posed by nuclear weapons. Their faces were drenched with sweat. Shin'ichi said to Mineko: "They're really making an effort. I'm so proud of these young people fighting for peace."

He then instructed one of the leaders accompanying him to arrange for cold soft drinks to be distributed to the young people. He also entrusted the leader with a message for the youth: "Thank you for your wonderful efforts in this hot weather. Please take care not to get sunstroke. I'm also fighting my hardest for peace. Let's keep up the fight together!"

The hard work of the youth division members bore fruit, and by September they had surpassed their goal by gathering eleven million signatures. Eventually, the petitions were collected from around the country. A sheaf containing ten thousand signatures measured 2.3 inches thick. If all the petitions were piled up together, it would form a stack 216 feet high.

A T THE END OF 1974, top youth division leaders gathered in a room at the Soka Gakkai Headquarters and held a long discussion about how to present the more than ten million signatures to the United Nations.

One young man suggested: "I don't think the full strength of our commitment to the abolition of nuclear weapons will be communicated just by mailing the petitions along with a letter to the U.N. secretary-general. It won't have that much impact."

The petitions embodied the hope of more than ten million individuals that nuclear armaments would be eliminated, and the youth leaders wanted to devise a method for the most effective way of delivering the signatures to the United Nations.

Another young man said: "For example, even if we had a representative deliver the petitions, it would be hard to get an appointment with the secretary-general and explain the significance of the signatures. However, if we are to truly communicate the passionate desire for peace of all who signed, it is absolutely essential that the petitions be passed directly to the secretary-general in person."

They couldn't think of a good solution. While they were puzzling over the matter, Soka Gakkai Student Division Leader Kaoru Tahara knocked on the door and entered the room.

"I have a message for you from President Yamamoto," he began. "He's been carefully observing our petition drive and knows that we're trying to think of the best way to deliver the signatures we've collected to the United Nations.

"Just a moment ago, President Yamamoto said to me: 'I am going to the United States in January of next year and will be meeting with U.N. Secretary-General Kurt Waldheim, and I would be happy to bring the petitions along with me. Please rest assured. Your efforts will definitely not go to waste. I am eager to help by applying the finishing touch to my disciples' project. This will be your mentor's challenge. I will personally deliver at least a portion of the petitions to the secretary-general.'

"So," Mr. Tahara concluded, "the petitions will definitely be handed directly to the secretary-general."

When the youth leaders heard this, their eyes lit up and they broke out into applause.

The mentor is always aware of the disciple's actions. Shin'ichi wished above all to repay his disciples' efforts as best he could.

AFTER MEETING with Secretary-General Waldheim, Shin'ichi held a press conference at the United Nations Headquarters. Replying to questions from the approximately fifty journalists packed into the room, Shin'ichi spoke of his hopes for the United Nations and his determination to support that organization. Then, following a meeting with Japan's ambassador to the United Nations, he attended a welcome reception held in his honor by the Japan Society of New York.

The Japan Society of New York had been established in 1907 as a private organization dedicated to promoting mutual understanding and cooperation between the peoples of Japan and the United States.

Eighty leaders from such fields as business and academia gathered for the reception, held at the society's Japan House. Shin'ichi had been asked to give a speech for the occasion. He spoke for some forty minutes about how a humanistic philosophy could usher in a new age.

Buddhism is a rich storehouse of wisdom that contains solutions to the complex problems of the age.

Pointing out that the advance of science and technology

has been accompanied by the rise of various threats to humanity, Shin'ichi emphasized that it is now crucial to focus on what it means to be human. He referred to comments by Club of Rome co-founder Aurélio Peccei (1908–84) on the need for a new humanism and the renaissance of the human spirit.

"The most daunting challenges of our time, including nuclear armaments and environmental pollution, can all be traced back to human greed, egotism and lack of self-control. In other words, they are the problems of humanity itself."

Shin'ichi stressed that Buddhist principles—which elucidate the essential nature of human beings and provide a practice for fundamentally transforming our lives—would be indispensible to spurring a renaissance of the human spirit. He added that the Buddhist phrase "all sentient beings" reflects the belief in the equality of all people and, furthermore, implies a commitment to striving with compassion and a sense of responsibility to help all people transform themselves at the most fundamental level and gain true inner happiness.

Shin'ichi then suggested a new direction that humanity should ultimately aim for, based on Buddhist principles: "First, in the latter half of the twentieth century, rather than hewing to the narrow self-interests of a single social system or nation, we need to adopt a value system with a global perspective and that embraces all humankind."

SHIN'ICHI'S VOICE gradually rose in intensity as he spoke: "Second, we need to recognize that each human being is, first and foremost, a living entity. This is an absolute and universal fact, transcending all such human characteristics as our social, ethnic or national identities. At the same time, individuals as social entities are largely conditioned by their times and their ethnic and national identities. Thus, in order to lead truly human lives, we must begin by affirming the major premise that we are all living entities and base ourselves on that.

"That is to say, in principle, we should base ourselves on the essential awareness that each human being is a living entity, while in action, we should strive in the real world to forge a universal solidarity that is undergirded by the shared ideal that, as living entities, we are all fellow members of the global family of humankind. I believe this is a perspective that is much needed by the world today."

For the audience, this was the first time they had heard these ideas stated in this way. They listened intently to Shin'ichi's remarks grounded in the Buddhist view of life, nodding in agreement.

Shin'ichi then explained that he initially called for the establishment of a "United Nations of Education" in order to provide education that will inspire and solidify an awareness of belonging to a global community that fundamentally supports ongoing international cooperation in various fields. He acknowledged that his ideas about building a universal solidarity embracing all humankind might be ridiculed as overly idealistic, considering the deep ideological divisions and nationalism prevalent in the world. Nonetheless, he reaffirmed his commitment to pursuing this "impossible dream" for as long as he lives.

The Indian poet Rabindranath Tagore (1861–1941), with his unbounded faith in human beings, once wrote,

"It is man's true function to make the impossible into the possible by dint of his own powers."[17] Shin'ichi shared this conviction. People shine when they strive to live up to great ideals.

Shin'ichi concluded his remarks by saying: "Humankind is certain to experience the fierce onslaught of many bitter winters in the future, as well. Unless we work together with unshakable conviction and courage to build a bastion of human solidarity for peace, we cannot expect a bright future ahead. It is my genuine wish to join hands with all humankind in shared purpose to take on this valiant endeavor."

WHEN SHIN'ICHI'S speech ended, the room resounded with enthusiastic applause. Many of those in attendance later said that they were glad to have had this opportunity to learn of the Soka Gakkai's ideal of humanism and were deeply impressed by it.

Shin'ichi was always in complete earnest. On this occasion, too, speaking as if he were addressing global leaders, he wholeheartedly elucidated a path for pioneering a new era guided by the wisdom of Buddhism. He had spent several days writing his speech, taking it through numerous drafts. He figured that it would probably be the first and only chance for most of the gathered members of the Japan Society to hear him speak, making his speech a very important, once-in-a-lifetime endeavor. Given that, Shin'ichi felt compelled to do his very best so that his speech would provide his listeners with an inspiring encounter with the philosophy of Buddhism. That is how he approached this opportunity—and, in fact, every occasion on which he spoke. Whether he was meeting with world leaders, encouraging members or attending various Soka Gakkai meetings, he always prepared thoroughly and exerted himself with all his might. By doing so, he was able to truly move and inspire people and win their sympathy and understanding.

This is the spirit that Soka Gakkai leaders should have whenever they talk to others or attend meetings.

On January 11, Shin'ichi traveled by train from New York City to Washington, D.C. On January 13, he visited the U.S. State Department, where he was scheduled to meet with Secretary of State Henry Kissinger. Shin'ichi was eagerly looking forward to this occasion because Secretary Kissinger was an individual with whom he fervently hoped to engage in a discussion about world peace.

In January 1973, Shin'ichi wrote a letter to U.S. President Richard Nixon urging the cessation of the Vietnam War and, through an intermediary, had it delivered to Mr. Kissinger, who, as President Nixon's national security advisor, passed it on to the president. Since then, Shin'ichi had exchanged letters with Mr. Kissinger on several occasions. In one of Mr. Kissinger's letters, the American diplomat had invited Shin'ichi to pay him a visit whenever he might be in the United States. When Shin'ichi informed Mr. Kissinger about his impending U.S. visit, Mr. Kissinger replied that he looked forward to meeting Shin'ichi, and thus their first encounter was arranged.

SNOW HAD BEEN falling since the morning of that day (January 13). The white dome of the United

States Capitol stood out boldly against the sky, a proud symbol of America, the land of liberty. The State Department is located near the Lincoln Memorial and less than one mile from the White House. The meeting between Secretary Kissinger and Shin'ichi took place in the secretary's office, starting at half past two that afternoon. Secretary Kissinger was very busy with preparations for U.S. President Gerald Ford's State of the Union address, but he found time to meet with Shin'ichi.

Shin'ichi began by thanking his host courteously for taking time out of his busy schedule to see him. Mr. Kissinger smiled and welcomed him heartily. Perhaps because they had already exchanged several letters, it was like a reunion of old friends, and the atmosphere was amicable and relaxed. "Let's start by taking a photograph," suggested Secretary Kissinger, and they sat together for the camera.

Then the secretary motioned Shin'ichi to take a seat on a sofa in the room. A table lamp with an arabesque design stood between them and, under its soft light, their discussion began. The only ones in the room were Shin'ichi, Secretary Kissinger and the interpreter supplied by the U.S. government.

Shin'ichi began by expressing his gratitude for the honorary citizenships he had been awarded by some forty municipalities and states across the United States. Mr. Kissinger smiled and replied that the American people were honored and happy to be able to bestow these accolades on Shin'ichi. His expression looked tired, though, no doubt because of the demands of his work.

When Shin'ichi began to talk about the current

international situation, however, Secretary Kissinger immediately perked up. Shin'ichi had been carefully observing Mr. Kissinger's activities since becoming President Nixon's national security advisor in January 1969. He knew that the American diplomat had a keen ability to read the times, was a sophisticated strategist and had a dynamic, active personality.

As thirty-fifth U.S. president John F. Kennedy once stated, change is action.[18]

U.S. SECRETARY of State Henry Kissinger was considered a coolheaded realist and the very antithesis of an idealist. In order to make our ideals a reality, we must first examine actual conditions. If we avert our eyes from reality, our ideals become nothing more than illusions. Secretary Kissinger held aloft the torch of ideals while standing firmly on the ground of reality, which is precisely why he was successful in transforming a number of realities that others thought would never change.

Shin'ichi could not forget that, in July 1971, as national security advisor, Mr. Kissinger embarked on a secret mission to Beijing, opening the way for the subsequent state visit by U.S. President Richard Nixon and the thawing of Sino–American relations. This act astonished the entire world, startling everyone by its boldness.

Mr. Kissinger was also a major player in the Strategic Arms Limitation Talks between the United States and the Soviet Union. He promoted the gradual withdrawal of U.S. troops from Vietnam and worked behind the scenes toward ending the conflict. Within all these actions, Shin'ichi saw a strong commitment to peace.

In 1938, at the age of fifteen, Mr. Kissinger emigrated

with his family from Germany to New York. Hitler was in power in Germany, and persecution of the Jews was intensifying daily. Being Jewish, the Kissinger family was also affected. Those leaving Germany were not allowed to bring anything of value with them, however, so the family arrived in the United States with little more than the clothes on their backs. Even so, they were still among the fortunate; more than a dozen of their relatives who remained in Germany died in the Nazi concentration camps.

Tossed about by the vicissitudes of the times, the Kissinger family struggled to survive in their new home. Mr. Kissinger's father had been a teacher, but he was unable to find a teaching position in the United States, so he got a clerical job in a factory. Though he worked very hard, he still had difficulty supporting his family. Young Henry also worked and attended high school at night. His youth was a time of great struggle, which contributed to his later success in life.

Second Soka Gakkai president Josei Toda taught us that physical and spiritual hardships make us stronger and that young people should not seek an easy or idle life.

AS HE ENDURED great hardship, Henry Kissinger built himself into a strong person who was unswayed by self-indulgent sentimentality, hatred or pessimism. He earned his degree from Harvard University and, gaining a reputation as a scholar of international politics, became a professor. Then U.S. President Richard Nixon appointed him as his national security advisor, and he began to be active in politics. In 1973, Henry Kissinger was lauded for his role in the signing of a peace accord between the United States and Vietnam, and he was awarded the Nobel Peace Prize. In the same year, he was appointed U.S. Secretary of State.

Shin'ichi was eager to talk at length with Secretary Kissinger for the sake of global peace and to try to discover with him a new direction for humanity. Mr. Kissinger had a rational, straightforward personality and cared little for empty formalities. He was a sharp-minded analyst who always grasped the essence of the question at hand, so their discussion proceeded at a brisk pace.

When Shin'ichi asked Mr. Kissinger what he thought about a peace and friendship treaty between Japan and China, the American diplomat immediately responded that he was in favor of it and thought it should be realized. During the encounter, Mr. Kissinger inquired of Shin'ichi: "Let me ask you frankly, where does your allegiance lie with regard to the world powers?" Clearly,

Mr. Kissinger's question was motivated by the fact that Shin'ichi had visited and met with the leaders of China and the Soviet Union and was now talking with him in the United States.

Shin'ichi replied unhesitatingly: "We are not affiliated with the Western or the Eastern bloc. Nor are we the allies of China, the Soviet Union or the United States. We are a force for peace, and we ally ourselves with humankind."

This was the humanism upon which Shin'ichi firmly based himself, and it was the fundamental position of the Soka Gakkai.

Mr. Kissinger smiled. It seemed he understood Shin'ichi's convictions. For the rest of their discussion, they talked about such topics as the Arab-Israeli conflict, Sino–American and Soviet–American relations and the Strategic Arms Limitation Talks. Their dialogue proceeded with the shared resonance of their wish to find pathways to peace.

AT THE MEETING, Shin'ichi hoped to offer several proposals for fostering peace in the Middle East, a region that had become a dangerous flash point in the world. The crisis there was not simply a regional matter, as it bore a serious impact on the governments and economies of every nation in the world, even having the potential to trigger a third world war. Shin'ichi had high expectations for Secretary Kissinger's earnest efforts to resolve the conflict and deeply hoped that the diplomat could forge lasting peace in the region.

Shin'ichi's proposals transcended specific points regarding the peace negotiations, articulating more fundamental and long-term policies for peace. His ideas were an expression of basic principles for achieving peace in the Middle East. The Arab-Israeli conflict had complex and deep-seated historical roots, and conditions had become like a tangled web. Temporary, stopgap measures no longer had any effect on solving the core issues. Therefore, Shin'ichi concentrated on articulating fundamental principles for peace rather than on suggesting specific concrete actions.

However, Shin'ichi did not want to take up Mr. Kissinger's precious time by attempting to hold a detailed discussion on such a complex matter during their meeting, so he had the proposals—about ten Japanese manuscript pages long—translated into English for presentation to the secretary of state. Shin'ichi was always considerate of those he spoke with, and he knew how busy his host was. Such consideration is a reflection of character.

Briefly summing up his thoughts on the Middle East situation, Shin'ichi handed the translated manuscript to the diplomat.

"May I look at it now?" asked Mr. Kissinger.

When Shin'ichi said he certainly could, Mr. Kissinger began to peruse the manuscript. After reading the entire document, he returned to the beginning and began reading it again.

Shin'ichi's first principle for peace in the Middle East was that the opinions of the people of the weaker nations must be given priority over the interests of the powerful nations. This is an iron rule for achieving peace.

Lasting peace in the Middle East would never be attained unless the rights of the Palestinians, who had become landless, were restored and their happiness made a priority.

I N HIS PROPOSAL, Shin'ichi referred to the vision of peaceful coexistence of Israelis and Palestinians that was articulated by the Polish Jewish writer and historian Isaac Deutscher. Since both sides had failed in their attempts to resolve their issues through the politics of ethnic identity, they would have to transcend their ethnic divisions in order to achieve peace. On that premise, Shin'ichi suggested that peaceful coexistence with the Palestinians would be possible if Israel became a more egalitarian society by securing freedom of thought, belief and religion for all, without discrimination due to ethnicity or birth. In support of this idea, he noted that, in the past, followers of Islam, Christianity and Judaism had lived peacefully side by side in the region.

The second basic principle Shin'ichi offered was that patient and steady negotiation, not force of arms, represented the only way to peace. The many outbreaks of violence in the Middle East until then had solved nothing, only making the situation more entrenched and desperate. Shin'ichi cited this to bolster his point that it was already evident that a military solution was not possible, and he strongly urged that the leaders of the big powers not encourage the use of force under any circumstances. Saying that no more ammunition should be allowed near the dangerous flash points in the region, he stated that nonmilitary financial and technical aid should be offered in lieu of armaments. He also proposed that the United States, the Soviet Union, the United Kingdom, France and other major oil-consuming nations should work together to establish a Middle East peacebuilding institute that would ensure and promote the peaceful development of the region.

Shin'ichi's third proposal was that specific negotiations aimed at creating a peaceful resolution should take place among the primary parties involved in the conflict. Negotiations carried out with the threat of military action by the great powers looming in the background would only lead to a temporary peace between wars. In that instance, any subsequent shift in the balance of military power in the region would spark a renewal of hostilities, fueled by dissatisfaction with the peace accord or ceasefire of the previous conflict.

SHIN'ICHI'S PROPOSAL also addressed the need for the United States and the Soviet Union to work toward having the primary parties of the conflict enter into direct negotiations. As for specific points to cover in such talks, however, he said that those should be decided through discussion among the primary parties, based on the principle of self-determination. Shin'ichi intentionally made no mention of such issues as the withdrawal of military forces or the recognition of nation-states. He believed that the primary parties involved should discuss and make those decisions themselves.

Also, in the document, Shin'ichi wrote that he hoped his proposals would be accepted as the heartfelt expression of a friend who eagerly desires peace for all humanity. And, reaffirming his personal commitment to global peace, Shin'ichi concluded the document by stating:

"Today, with every change in the situation in the Middle East, the world is observing your every action with bated breath. In my heart, I pray that your efforts to create peace in the Middle East will blossom profusely and bear fruit, so that the people experiencing ceaseless conflict in the region, as well as the poor and unfortunate people of the have-not nations around the globe, will applaud your success with appreciation and joy."

Secretary Kissinger read the document three times and then looked up: "Please give me a few days to consider what you have written here. And next time, I hope you will also make suggestions concerning the problem of oil. I also promise to convey your ideas to the president."

With gratitude and respect, Shin'ichi said: "Thank you very much. I am sure you must be tired because of your many pressing duties, and I know you face many daunting challenges, but please continue to strive courageously for world peace. If necessary, I am willing to go wherever I may be of help."

Lastly, Shin'ichi said, "Please convey my best regards to your wife."

"Thank you, thank you," replied the secretary with a soft smile.

Seeing that beaming smile, Shin'ichi felt as if he had really communicated with Henry Kissinger the man. Pleasant, smiling dialogue binds hearts even closer together.

WITH A SMILE, Secretary Kissinger said to Shin'ichi: "I'd like to meet with you again, as friends. Let's keep in touch. Please come visit me whenever you are in the United States."

From that meeting on, Shin'ichi's friendship with Mr. Kissinger deepened further. Even after Mr. Kissinger stepped down as secretary of state, they kept in contact and, motivated by their shared desire for world peace, met for discussions on several occasions at such places as the Soka Gakkai International Friendship Center in Tokyo's Shibuya Ward and the Seikyo Shimbun Building in neighboring Shinjuku Ward.

In September 1987, their dialogue, *Heiwa to jinsei to tetsugaku wo kataru* (Dialogue on Peace, Life and Philosophy)[19] was published.

They also held talks at a New York City hotel in June 1996. Mr. Kissinger came to the meeting knowing that Shin'ichi would be traveling from the United States to Cuba, where he would meet with President Fidel Castro.

At the time, the socialist state of Cuba was isolated on the world stage following the rapid collapse of the Soviet Union and the socialist governments in Eastern Europe. Moreover, in February of that year, two private American planes had been shot down near Cuba, causing a significant increase in bilateral tensions.

Mentioning his desire to see an improvement in U.S.–Cuban relations, Mr. Kissinger conveyed his strong expectations for Shin'ichi's visit. With those thoughts in mind, Shin'ichi flew to Cuba and met with President Castro. He also communicated Mr. Kissinger's views to the Cuban leader, and they enjoyed a fruitful dialogue for peace.

As the American Renaissance philosopher Ralph Waldo Emerson once wrote, "Friendship and association are very fine things, and a grand phalanx of the best of the human race, banded for some catholic object: yes, excellent."[20] Dialogue opens the way to new friendship. Fostering friendship brings the world and its people closer together.

After meeting with Secretary Kissinger at the U.S. State Department, Shin'ichi went to pay his respects to Deputy Secretary of State Robert Ingersoll, a former U.S. ambassador to Japan. Next, Shin'ichi went to the Japanese embassy, where he was scheduled to meet with Japanese Finance Minister Masayoshi Ohira, who was then visiting the United States.

JAPANESE FINANCE Minister Masayoshi Ohira was in Washington, D.C., to attend a gathering of finance ministers from developed nations, among other events. He sent word to Shin'ichi that he would like to meet with him at the Japanese Embassy. It would be Shin'ichi's first encounter with the finance minister.

After Shin'ichi arrived at the embassy and exchanged greetings with Mr. Ohira, the finance minister asked in a dispassionate tone, "President Yamamoto, I would like to hear your views on a Japan-China peace and friendship treaty."

Just one month prior, in December 1974, Mr. Ohira had become the finance minister in the cabinet of Prime Minister Takeo Miki. He had been foreign minister in the cabinet of Prime Minister Kakuei Tanaka when Japan–China diplomatic relations were normalized in 1972 and had also played a major role in opening air routes linking the two countries. Mr. Ohira now considered the matter of concluding a bilateral peace and friendship treaty as an issue of the most pressing importance.

The Joint Communiqué of the Government of Japan and the Government of the People's Republic of China that was announced in September 1972 specifically calls for both parties to enter into negotiations aimed at reaching agreement on a peace and friendship treaty. The first session of preliminary negotiations for such a treaty was conducted in November 1974, and a second session was scheduled to take place that month (January 1975). Prime Minister Miki also hoped to conclude a treaty, but other elements in his political party were vehemently opposed and progress was difficult. Mr. Miki's base within his party was too weak to push the matter forward.

The effort to improve bilateral relations was an incredibly demanding and even dangerous endeavor. When Mr. Ohira was working for the normalization of bilateral relations during his term as foreign minister, threatening letters were sent to his home. Far from intimidating him, however, this only spurred him to strengthen his resolve, and he dedicated himself to the task despite the personal risks involved. In the course of opening air routes connecting Japan and China, as well, he was repeatedly attacked by opposing factions within his own party.

Shin'ichi, too, had received innumerable threats and been subjected to storms of criticism and slander from the moment he set out toward constructing a bridge of bilateral friendship. As such, he understood Mr. Ohira's feelings and determination.

As the French writer Victor Hugo declared, "We who believe, what can we fear?"[21] This was Shin'ichi's conviction, as well. Those who live to achieve something great must be prepared to face difficulties. Nothing worthwhile can be accomplished without courage.

SHIN'ICHI SPOKE frankly and without reservation to Minister Ohira: "It is my sincere hope that a Japan-China peace and friendship treaty be concluded as quickly as possible."

Shin'ichi had been urging this for some time. In 1969, the year after he had first called for the normalization of diplomatic relations between Japan and China, he had proposed in "War and Peace," the fifth volume of his serialized novel *The Human Revolution*, that a peace and friendship treaty be concluded. While a bridge had been built with the normalization of bilateral relations in 1972, it was still a rough and shaky one, much like a rope bridge spanning a gorge. Shin'ichi believed that a peace and friendship treaty would form the foundation of an indestructible golden bridge that would endure for generations to come.

Shin'ichi added, "I just met with U.S. Secretary of State Henry Kissinger, and he was of the opinion that Japan and China should sign a peace and friendship treaty."

Mr. Ohira replied: "Yes, that is correct. It appears Chinese Premier Zhou Enlai asked Secretary Kissinger to support the treaty."

Shin'ichi recalled the way in which the ill Chinese leader had summoned all his strength to speak with him at the hospital in Beijing. Premier Zhou had said, "I hope that a peace and friendship treaty between our two countries can be signed as quickly as possible." Premier Zhou's voice resonated with his ardent wish that this be achieved within his lifetime.

Thinking of the Chinese premier, Shin'ichi said to Minister Ohira: "This is something that absolutely must be accomplished. Everyone is counting on you, Minister Ohira."

Mr. Ohira spoke with resolve: "I will see a peace and friendship treaty concluded. But it is going to take some time. We may not be able to do it this year. The real problem is not between Japan and China but within Japan itself. There is fierce conservative opposition to sincere efforts to promote bilateral friendship. Though Prime Minister Miki would like to realize such a treaty, he has very few supporters."

Shin'ichi stated emphatically: "The Japanese people are his supporters. Every citizen who desires peace is his supporter. We will back him up."

Public opinion will eventually ally itself with good judgment and just convictions, and that is why it is essential to continuously strive with an invincible spirit. Shin'ichi vowed to himself to give his all behind the scenes so that a bilateral peace and friendship treaty could be concluded.

LOOKING INTENTLY at Shin'ichi, Finance Minister Masayoshi Ohira nodded repeatedly in agreement. Shin'ichi continued: "The Japan-China peace and friendship treaty is extremely important not only for the two countries but also for the entire world. A declaration of peace and friendship between socialist China and capitalist Japan would be a landmark event. Humanity will not remain in this cold war era forever."

"That is very true," affirmed Mr. Ohira. "The times call for us to recognize that the world is one."

Shin'ichi's talk with the finance minister became an opportunity for the two men to affirm their shared commitment to bilateral friendship.

The path to the formal signing of the Japan-China Peace and Friendship Treaty was a thorny one indeed. Just as Minister Ohira had foreseen, negotiations nearly ran aground in February of that year [1975] over the issue of whether to include the anti-hegemony clause in the treaty. This clause, from the joint communiqué issued by Japan and China, stated that neither should seek hegemony in the Asia-Pacific region, and that each was opposed to efforts by any other country or group of countries to establish such hegemony. When the joint communiqué was announced, the Soviet Union protested to the Japanese government that the anti-hegemony clause was actually directed against the Soviet Union and represented an anti-Soviet declaration by both China and Japan. This sparked debate within Japan that the anti-hegemony clause should not be included in the treaty. The Chinese, however, were insistent upon its inclusion. Consensus on this point seemed difficult.

Eventually, appropriate steps were taken to reassure the Soviet Union, and the Japan-China Peace and Friendship Treaty was signed with the anti-hegemony clause intact in August 1978, ten years after Shin'ichi had called out for the normalization of diplomatic relations between Japan and China. At the time of the signing, Takeo Fukuda was the Japanese prime minister, and Masayoshi Ohira was the secretary-general of the Liberal Democratic Party. The treaty marked a significant step in the history of Sino–Japanese relations. The undercurrents of the times had now been made to flow swiftly toward peace. Shin'ichi applauded this achievement.

As the eminent physicist Albert Einstein observed about the process of creating peace: "Enduring peace will come about, not by countries continuing to threaten one another, but only through an honest effort to create mutual trust."[22]

ON JANUARY 14, Shin'ichi visited Arlington National Cemetery in the United States, where he laid a wreath at the Tomb of the Unknown Soldier. The skies were a clear blue, but the temperature was a frigid twenty-eight degrees Fahrenheit. In accord with Japanese custom, Shin'ichi removed his overcoat before offering the wreath. His ears ached in the cold.

Not only in the Soviet Union, he thought to himself, *but here, too, many young soldiers lie in rest. There are no winners or losers in war. All are sacrificed. What purpose can war ever serve? Who can it benefit?*

In countries everywhere, families who have lost loved ones suffer the same grief. War is the greatest evil that human beings can perpetrate. Buddhism points out how to vanquish the diabolic nature that causes war. Therefore, it is the mission of all Buddhists to rid the world of war. That is the only way to repay the sacrifices of those who rest here.

With a profound commitment to lasting peace in his heart, Shin'ichi laid his wreath before the Tomb of the Unknown Soldier and observed a moment of silence, the honor guard looking on. He solemnly chanted Nam-myoho-renge-kyo three times and then repeated this twice more. Afterward, he said, "I prayed that there would never be another war."

Shin'ichi also offered prayers at the graves of thirty-fifth U.S. President John F. Kennedy (1917–63) and his brother Robert F. Kennedy (1925–68), both of whom are buried at Arlington. Looking back, he deeply regretted that his appointment to meet and talk with President Kennedy could not be realized.

Following his visit to Washington, D.C., Shin'ichi flew to Chicago, Los Angeles and Honolulu, finally heading for Guam on January 23. Soka Gakkai members from fifty-one countries and territories around the globe were scheduled to gather in Guam on January 26 for the First World Peace Conference. The curtain was rising on a new phase of the movement for peace.

As John F. Kennedy once declared, "United, there is little we cannot do in a host of cooperative ventures."[23] The greatest endeavor that humanity could ever unite and strive for is the construction of lasting peace. Deep in his heart, Shin'ichi was firmly resolved to create the bonds that would form the core of the solidarity needed to make this achievement possible.

Notes:

1. Lu Hsun, "Regret for the Past," in *Selected Stories of Lu Hsun,* translated by Yang Xianyi and Gladys Yang (New York: W. W. Norton and Company, Inc., 2003), p. 204.

2. Translated from Chinese. Lu Xun, "Po e sheng lun" (On Defeating the Voices of Evil), in *Lu Xun quanji* (The Complete Works of Lu Xun) (Beijing: Renmin wenxue chuban-she, 1996), vol. 8, p. 26.

3. Mahatma Gandhi, *The Collected Works of Mahatma Gandhi* (New Delhi: The Publications Division, Ministry of Information and Broadcasting, Government of India, 1966), vol. 20, p. 370.

4. Translated from Japanese. Soong Ching-ling, *So Keirei sen-shu* (Selected Writings of Soong Ching-ling), translated by Fumiko Niki (Tokyo: Domesu Shuppan, 1979), p. 551.

5. Leo Tolstoy, *A Calendar of Wisdom,* translated by Peter Seki-rin (New York: Scribner, 1997), p. 343.

6. Mahatma Gandhi, *The Collected Works of Mahatma Gandhi* (New Delhi: Publications Division, Ministry of Information and Broadcasting, Government of India, 1979), vol. 76 (April 1, 1942–December 17, 1942), p. 396.

7. Leo Tolstoy, *What to Do?,* translated by Isabel F. Hapgood (n.a.: Aegypan Press, 2006), p. 197.

8. Translated from Chinese. http://edu.stuccess.com/Know-Center/EduForum/lilun/mingzhu/taoxingzhi/00000003.htm (December 19, 2007).

9. Translated from Japanese. Alfred Stucki, *Hiruti den* (A Life of

Hilty), translated by Koji Kunimatsu and Toshio Ito (Tokyo: Hakusui-sha, 1959), p. 74.

10. Johann Wolfgang von Goethe, *Conversations of Goethe with Johann Peter Eckermann,* translated by John Oxenford and edited by J. K. Moorhead (New York: Da Capo Press, 1998), p. 248.

11. *The I-Ching, or Book of Changes,* translated by Cary F. Baynes (Princeton, New Jersey: Princeton University Press, 1977), p. 59.

12. http://www.etext.org/Politics/MIM/classics/mao/cpc/constitution1975.html (January 8, 2008).

13. http://www.marxists.org/reference/archive/zhou-enlai/1975/01/13.htm (January 8, 2008).

14. Translated from Japanese. Ba Jin, *Pakin kaioku-shu* (Collected Reminiscences of Ba Jin), edited and translated by Takeo Ikeda (Tokyo: Akiyama Shoten, 1978), p. 157.

15. Translated from Japanese. Yukio Ozaki, *Ozaki Gakudo zenshu* (Collected Writings of Gakudo Ozaki) (Tokyo: Koronsha, 1955), vol. 10, p. 312.

16. http://www.time.com/time/magazine/article/0,9171,917065-1,00.html (January 9, 2008).

17. Rabindranath Tagore, *The English Writings of Rabindranath Tagore, Volume 3: A Miscellany,* edited by Sisir Kumar Das (New Delhi: Sahitya Akademi, 1996), p. 413.

18. See http://www.jfklink.com/speeches/jfk/sept60/jfk060960_seattle01.html (January 16, 2008).

19. Currently available only in Japanese. Daisaku Ikeda and Henry Kissinger, *Heiwa to jinsei to tetsugaku wo kataru* (Dialogue on Peace, Life, and Philosophy) (Tokyo: Ushio Publishing Company, 1987).

20. Ralph Waldo Emerson, "New England Reformers," in *Essays and Lectures* (New York: Library of America, 1983), p. 598.

21. Victor Hugo, *Les Misérables,* translated by Lee Fahnestock and Norman MacAfee (New York: New American Library, 1987), p. 1000.

22. Albert Einstein, *Einstein on Peace,* edited by Otto Nathan and Heinz Norden (New York: Avenal Books, 1981), p. 380.

23. John Fitzgerald Kennedy, *Legacy of a President: The Memorable Words of John Fitzgerald Kennedy* (Washington, D. C.: United States Information Agency, 1964), p. 11.

Index

More on Nichiren Buddhism
and Its Application to Daily Life

The following fifteen titles can be purchased from your local
or online bookseller, or go to the Middleway Press Web site
(www.middlewaypress.com).

The Buddha in Your Mirror: Practical Buddhism and the Search for Self
by Woody Hochswender, Greg Martin and Ted Morino
A best-selling Buddhist primer that reveals the most modern, effective and practical way to achieve what is called enlightenment or Buddhahood. Based on the centuries-old teaching of the Japanese Buddhist master Nichiren, this method has been called the "direct path" to enlightenment.
(Paperback: ISBN 978-0-9674697-8-2; $14.00,
Hardcover: ISBN 978-0-9674697-1-3; $23.95)

The Buddha Next Door:
Ordinary People, Extraordinary Stories
by Zan Gaudioso and Greg Martin
These first-person narratives—representing people from throughout the country of various ages and ethnic backgrounds—examine the challenges of daily life associated with health, relationships, career and aging, and the ensuing experiences of hope, success, inspiration and personal enlightenment that come about as a result of living as Nichiren Buddhists.
(Paperback: ISBN 978-0-9779245-1-6; $15.95)

Buddhism Day by Day: Wisdom for Modern Life
by Daisaku Ikeda

This treasury of practical information and encouragement will appeal to those seeking a deeper understanding of how to apply the tenets of Nichiren Buddhism in their day-to-day lives.

(Paperback: ISBN 978-0-9723267-5-9; $15.95)

Buddhism, the First Millennium
by Daisaku Ikeda

Understanding the early history of Buddhism comes as much from an appreciation of the spirit imparted by its founder as from extant facts, theories and legends. Author Daisaku Ikeda pieces together the fabric of events with insightful conjecture to illuminate how and why Buddhism came to be a major world religion.

(Paperback: ISBN 978-0-9779245-3-0; $14.95)

Buddhism for You series

In this oasis of insight and advice on the power of Nichiren Buddhism—which holds that everyone has a Buddha nature of limitless power, wisdom and compassion—readers will learn how to live a life filled with courage, determination, love and prayer to achieve their goals and desires.

(**Courage** Hardcover: ISBN 978-0-9723267-6-6; $7.95)
(**Determination** Hardcover: ISBN 978-0-9723267-8-0; $7.95)
(**Love** Hardcover: ISBN 978-0-9723267-7-3; $7.95)
(**Prayer** Hardcover: ISBN 978-0-9723267-9-7; $7.95)

Choose Hope: Your Role in Waging Peace in the Nuclear Age
by David Krieger and Daisaku Ikeda

"In this nuclear age, when the future of humankind is imperiled by irrational strategies, it is imperative to restore sanity to our policies and hope to our destiny. Only a rational analysis of our problems can lead to their solution. This book is an example par excellence of a rational approach."

—Joseph Rotblat, Nobel Peace Prize laureate

(Hardcover: ISBN 978-0-9674697-6-8; $23.95)

The Flower of Chinese Buddhism
by Daisaku Ikeda

Author Daisaku Ikeda crafts a lively narrative of the traders and monks who first brought Buddhism to China along the Silk Road, the first Chinese Buddhist leaders, the development of distinctly Chinese schools of Buddhism—highlighting the Tiantai school, which was later influential in Japan—and the eventual decline of Buddhism in China after harsh persecution in the tenth century. *The Flower of Chinese Buddhism* illuminates the role of Buddhism in Chinese society and, by extension, in human society in general, charting a course that religion must follow to respond to the needs of the times, then and now.

(Paperback: ISBN 978-0-9779245-4-7; $14.95)

The Living Buddha: An Interpretive Biography
by Daisaku Ikeda

An intimate portrayal of one of history's most important and obscure figures, the Buddha, *The Living Buddha* chronicle reveals him not as a mystic, but a warm and engaged human being that was very much the product of his turbulent times. This biographical account traces the path of Siddhartha Gautama as he walked away from the pleasure palace that had been his home and joined a growing force of wandering monks, ultimately making his way toward enlightenment beneath the *bodhi* tree, and spending the next forty-five years sharing his insights along the banks of the Ganges.

(Paperback: ISBN 978-0-9779245-2-3; $14.95)

Planetary Citizenship: *Your* Values, Beliefs and Actions *Can* Shape a Sustainable World
by Hazel Henderson and Daisaku Ikeda

"*Planetary Citizenship* is a delightful introduction to some of the most important ideas and facts concerning stewardship of the planet. I cannot think of any book that deals with more important issues."

—Mihaly Csikszentmihalyi, author of *Flow: The Psychology of Optimal Experience,* California

(Hardcover: ISBN 978-0-9723267-2-8; $23.95)

Romancing the Buddha: Embracing Buddhism in My Everyday Life by Michael Lisagor

"*Romancing the Buddha: Embracing Buddhism in My Everyday Life* provides excellent insights into applying Nichiren Buddhism to the difficulties of daily life, including depression, spousal illness, the challenge of raising two daughters and the quest for happiness. An absorbing and inspirational selection of vignettes touched with wisdom, *Romancing the Buddha* is an impressive and welcome contribution to Buddhist Studies reading lists."
—Midwest Book Review
(Paperback: ISBN 978-0-9723267-4-2; $18.95)

Unlocking the Mysteries of Birth & Death... and Everything In Between, A Buddhist View of Life (second edition) by Daisaku Ikeda

"In this slender volume, Mr. Ikeda presents a wealth of profound information in a clear and straightforward style that can be easily absorbed by the interested lay reader. His life's work, and the underlying purpose of his book, is simply to help human beings derive maximum meaning from their lives through the study of Buddhism."
—ForeWord Magazine
(Paperback: ISBN 978-0-9723267-0-4; $15.00)

The Way of Youth: Buddhist Common Sense for Handling Life's Questions by Daisaku Ikeda

"[This book] shows the reader how to flourish as a young person in the world today; how to build confidence and character in modern society; learn to live with respect for oneself and others; how to contribute to a positive, free and peaceful society; and find true personal happiness."
—Midwest Book Review
(Paperback: ISBN 978-0-9674697-0-6; $14.95)

The following titles can be purchased at SGI-USA
bookstores nationwide or through the mail order center:
call 800-626-1313 or e-mail mailorder@sgi-usa.org.

Faith into Action: Thoughts on Selected Topics
by Daisaku Ikeda
A collection of inspirational excerpts arranged by subject. Perfect for finding just the right quote to encourage yourself or a friend or when preparing for a meeting.
(World Tribune Press, mail order #4135; $12.95)

The Human Revolution boxed set by Daisaku Ikeda
"A great human revolution in just a single individual will help achieve a change in the destiny of a nation, and further, can even enable a change in the destiny of all humankind." With this as his main theme, the author wrote his twelve-volume account of Josei Toda's life and the phenomenal growth of the Soka Gakkai in postwar Japan. Published in a slightly abridged two-book set, this work paints a fascinating and empowering story of the far-reaching effects of one person's inner determination. Josei Toda's awakening and transformation, his efforts to teach others the unlimited power of faith, his dedication in leading thousands out of misery and poverty, the efforts of his devoted disciple, Shin'ichi Yamamoto—within these stories we find the keys for building lives of genuine happiness.
(World Tribune Press, mail order #4182; $45.00)

The Journey Begins: First Steps in Buddhist Practice
A pamphlet on the basics of Nichiren Buddhism. Each step is discussed in very basic terms, but each plays an important role in one's practice.
(World Tribune Press, $1.00 per pamphlet)
[Chinese] mail order #4186
[English] mail order #4138
[French] mail order #4188
[Japanese] mail order #4193
[Spanish] mail order #4139

Kaneko's Story: A Conversation with Kaneko Ikeda
Kaneko Ikeda shares thoughts and stories of her youth, marriage and family and of supporting her husband of more than fifty-five years, SGI President Daisaku Ikeda. Also included are four messages written to the women of the SGI.
(World Tribune Press, mail order #234302; $9.95)

My Dear Friends in America by Daisaku Ikeda
This volume brings together for the first time all of the SGI president's speeches to U.S. members in the 1990s.
(World Tribune Press, Paperback: SKU #204891; $15.95)

My Path of Youth by Hiromasa Ikeda
This book presents a selection of essays by Hiromasa Ikeda that were published in Japanese in the *Koko Shimpo*, the Soka Gakkai's high school division newspaper. In them, he conveys his message to youth by way of recounting memories of his childhood and as a young man. Hiromasa Ikeda also shares his views on the spirit of the mentor–disciple relationship in Buddhism, the significance of his father's work and mission, and the importance of living based on a resolve for peace.
(World Tribune Press, mail order #234476; $9.95)

The New Human Revolution by Daisaku Ikeda
An ongoing novelized history of the Soka Gakkai, which contains not only episodes from the past but guidance in faith that we can apply as we grow our movement here in the United States.
(World Tribune Press; $12.00 each volume)
Volume 1, mail order #4601
Volume 2, mail order #4602
Volume 3, mail order #4603
Volume 4, mail order #4604
Volume 5, mail order #4605
Volume 6, mail order #4606
Volume 7, mail order #4607
Volume 8, mail order #4608

Volume 9, mail order #4609
Volume 10, mail order #4610
Volume 11, mail order #4611
Volume 12, mail order #4612
Volume 13, mail order #4613
Volume 14, mail order #4614
Volume 15, mail order #275446
Volume 16, SKU #275447
Volume 17, SKU #275448
Volume 18, SKU #275449
Volume 19, SKU #275450
Volume 20, SKU #275451

The Winning Life: An Introduction to Buddhist Practice

Using plain language, this booklet gives a quick-yet-detailed intro-
duction to a winning way of life based on Nichiren Daishonin's
teachings. A perfect tool for introducing others to the benefits of
practice.
(World Tribune Press, $1.00 per booklet)
[Armenian] mail order #4189
[Chinese] mail order #4107
[English] mail order #4105
[French] mail order #4187
[Japanese] mail order #4815
[Korean] mail order #4113
[Spanish] mail order #4106

The Wisdom of the Lotus Sutra, vols. I–VI

by Daisaku Ikeda, Katsuji Saito, Takanori Endo
and Haruo Suda
A captivating dialogue on the twenty-eight-chapter Lotus Sutra
that brings this ancient writing's important messages into practical
application for daily life and for realizing a peaceful world.
(World Tribune Press, $10.95 per volume)
Volume I, mail order #4281
Volume II,mail order #4282

Volume III, mail order #4283
Volume IV, mail order #4284
Volume V, mail order #4285
Volume VI, mail order #4286

The World of Nichiren Daishonin's Writings, vols 1–4

by Daisaku Ikeda, Katsuji Saito and Masaaki Morinaka

These books bring to life the teachings and major life events of Nichiren Daishonin through an ongoing discussion between SGI President Ikeda, Soka Gakkai Study Department Leader Katsuji Saito and Study Department Vice Leader Masaaki Morinaka.

(SGI Malaysia, $7.95 per volume)

Volume 1, mail order #1891
Volume 2, mail order #1892
Volume 3, mail order #1893
Volume 4, mail order #1894

A Youthful Diary: One Man's Journey From the Beginning of Faith to Worldwide Leadership for Peace

by Daisaku Ikeda

Youthful inspiration for people of all ages. Through the tale of the ever-deepening relationship between the young Daisaku Ikeda and his mentor-in-life, Josei Toda, *A Youthful Diary* is a compelling account of both triumphs and setbacks on the road to establishing the foundation of today's Soka Gakkai.

(World Tribune Press, Paperback: mail order #4120; $15.00)